DATE DUE

MAR 7			
MAR 16			
GAYLORD			PRINTED IN U.S.A.

THAT DUNBAR BOY

The Story of America's Famous Negro Poet

Also by Jean Gould

YOUNG MARINER MELVILLE

That Dunbar Boy

THE STORY OF
AMERICA'S FAMOUS NEGRO POET

By JEAN GOULD

Illustrated by Charles Walker

DODD, MEAD & COMPANY • NEW YORK • 1958

The poems quoted in this book are from
The Complete Poems of Paul Laurence Dunbar
Copyright 1903, 1904, 1905, 1913
by Dodd, Mead & Company

Library of Congress Catalog Card Number: 58-13085

Printed in the United States of America
by The Cornwall Press, Inc., Cornwall, N. Y.

*This story of a boy who enjoyed happy school days
is dedicated to school children everywhere*

Contents

vii

THAT DUNBAR BOY

The Story of America's Famous Negro Poet

"Scamp"

SMALL PAUL was no higher than Ma's kitchen table, but he had a houseful of love and laughter in his heart. He loved Ma's stories, he loved to sing—and he loved mischief.

One hot sultry evening in the summer of 1876, he was sitting in Ma's carpet-back rocker, watching her iron, and wishing his half-brothers, Rob and Buddy, would come home in time to play with him before bed. He had wanted to go along with them, but as usual, they said he was "too little." And Ma had sided with them; she was afraid Paul would get hurt if he went to play with the older boys. He sighed, studying her as she set her iron on the woodstove, took off the handle with a little snap, and fastened it on the hot one waiting there; she looked like a fireman when she "changed" irons.

Ma was always ironing, it seemed to Paul. That was because she did washing and ironing to earn most of the family living; Pa was a Civil War veteran who could find nothing but odd jobs after the war was over, and they did not bring in much. As a rule, Ma would tell Paul stories while she did her work—tales of the days when she was "a little girl in Kentucky"—and Paul liked nothing better than listening to Ma's stories. But tonight she had promised one of her best customers she would have the "wash" done and delivered ahead of time for a special occasion. She had to whisk through the ironing so fast she couldn't take time to "rec'lect" things that happened long ago.

Hearing Paul sigh, she looked up. " 'Bout time those two showed up; they're late now," she remarked, meaning Buddy and Rob. (It was wonderful the way Ma could read your thoughts.) "I told them to be back before dark."

"Maybe the Boogah Man's got 'em," Paul said, ready to make up an adventure story. "Maybe he reached out and grabbed 'em when they came around the corner, and they can't get away."

Ma chuckled. "More likely the sandman's got 'em," she said. "Paul, why don't you go out on the front porch and holler 'em home?"

He needed no second invitation. It made him feel important to call his brothers in. He slid out of the rocker, and did a few skips around the room before heading for the doorway that led to the dark front of the house. He was wearing a pair of faded, patched overalls that Ma had cut down from some old ones of Rob's. (Until this summer he had worn hand-me-down baby dresses because Ma couldn't take the time to fix over the boys' clothes for him.) Below the overalls his skipping brown feet were bare; and above them his neat, round woolly head bounced like an India rubber ball. His great dark eyes, so often dreamy, were dancing like an imp's. An idea had come to him.

"Run along, you," Ma said, laughing. "And mind you don't go away from that porch!"

"I won't Ma," he answered as he skipped through the doorway. He had no intention of going *away* from the porch—he was going *under* it. He pushed open the rusty screen door and stepped out into the night.

It was very quiet on Howard Street, in the east end of the town—Dayton, Ohio—where the Dunbars lived. The only light came dimly from a wavering gas lamp at the far end of the block, which just pierced the darkness around it, and made the trees send strange, quivering shadows across the road. Paul peered up and down, looking for his brothers, but he didn't call them. That would spoil everything. Soon he saw the two boys turning the corner under the gas lamp.

He stole down the steps and through a hole in the wooden lattice work under the porch. Putting his eye up to one of the openings in the lattice, he crouched in he blackness without making a sound until he spotted the boys' legs as they neared the house.

Then he let out an eerie cry. "Woo-oo! Woo-oo!"

Buddy stopped, putting his hand on Rob's arm. "What's that?"

"I dunno—owl, maybe," Rob said, careless-like, but his voice was not quite steady.

Paul put his hand over his mouth to keep from giggling. "Woo-oo, woo-oo!" he went once more.

"There it is again!" Buddy whispered. "Think it's an owl?"

"I can't tell," Rob whispered back. They stood at the top of the path up to the house, hesitating.

Paul was about to chant, "I'm the Boogah Man," when Ma's voice boomed, "Paul! Paul!" and a moment later she appeared in the doorway to find out why she hadn't heard him calling.

"Oh, there you are, boys," she said seeing Buddy and Rob. "Where's Paul? I sent him out here to holler for you."

From beneath the floor came the weird cry, "woo-woo-oo."

The boys burst into a shout and ran toward the porch.

Rob bent down by the gap in the lattice. "Come on out, Paul," he said.

"I'm the Boogah Man," Paul chanted, laughing gleefully as he slipped out between the slats. "Fooled you that time!"

The boys laughed, too, but they insisted they had known all along it was Paul. Then Ma herded them all into the house and said it was high time for bed.

"Pretty soon Pa'll be coming home, and you know he won't want to hear anyone stirring," she reminded them.

A stern man, much older than Ma, Pa had no patience with the nonsense of small boys, and liked things quiet when he came into the house. So the three of them heeded her warning and started for bed, Paul following the two older ones.

"Can't we have some cornpone first, Ma?" Buddy asked at the door of their room.

Paul and Rob chimed in with him, but Ma shook her head. 'Sorry, boys—the co'npone's gone. You had it all for supper."

"Co'npone's gone," Paul repeated. "Co'npone's gone." He loved rhyming words. He made a song of them, dancing around Ma, who laughed in spite of herself as she shooed him off to bed. She knew the boys must be hungry; too often there was not enough food to fill the stomachs of growing children, and it worried her. But Paul could always make her laugh; he was a joy forever.

He had been born four years before, on June 27, 1872. It had been a hot, sultry day such as this, Ma remembered, and the bees hummed lazily in the honeysuckle vine outside the bedroom window. Pa's face, as he bent over to examine the baby, was shining with perspiration. And pride! This was his first child. (Rob, or Robert, and Buddy, whose real name was William, were Ma's boys by her first marriage; their father had disappeared during the war.)

Pa, who bore the old Biblical name of Joshua, wanted to call the baby Paul; perhaps his son would follow in the footsteps of the Apostle and become a preacher. Ma had more romantic ideas; she thought of the fine names in the poems the plantation owner used to read aloud back in Kentucky, and she wanted to call the baby Laurence. Perhaps her son would be a world traveler, and come home to write his adventures in splendid poems. Ma, who had been plain Matilda all her life, wanted this baby to have an unusual name. But Pa was firm; "Paul was a great man," he said. "This child will be great some day and do you honor."

Ma did not give up completely. "At least let Laurence be in the middle," she had insisted softly. And Pa agreed.

So Paul Laurence Dunbar it was—a little high-sounding, maybe, the neighbors thought, but to Ma it sounded like a song.

Paul was a good baby, and a smart one, although he was not very strong, the way Rob and Buddy had been. His eyes were bright, and almost anything could make him smile. He picked up words before he was one, but he caught the "croup" several times during the first year and he didn't have the strength to run around as soon as the others had. Once he began, however, he was like a cricket around the house—merry, chirping, and a great comfort to Ma.

When he was two and a half a baby sister, Elizabeth, had been born, and before long he was able to mind the baby for Ma, rocking the old wooden cradle back and forth with his foot the way she had shown him. He was quick to learn, and skillful once he got the hang of doing a thing. If the baby cried, he rocked the cradle faster, or he tried to shush her with a little song, as he had heard Ma do.

But Elizabeth was more frail and thin than Paul had been, and after a time it took more than fast rocking or a lullaby to soothe her whimpering. She was sick, and Ma couldn't care for her properly. There was no money for a doctor or medicine.

Then one night not too long ago, the little girl had died, and Paul had become the baby in the family again. Ma watched over him as much as she could, with all the work she had to do. She even took on rush jobs, as she had tonight, so she could earn a few extra pennies for cream once in a while to put some fat on his bones, though it didn't help much. His legs stayed skinny as pipe stems, and his ribs stuck out like slats down both sides of his chest. If he had a cold, Ma kept him indoors, and if he had a fever, she put him to bed and fed him tea. In the winter, she was afraid to let him play in the snow because he might get chilled. And in the summer she didn't let him play too hard outdoors because he might get overheated. She probably was "too finicky about that boy," as Pa said, but she was not really spoiling him. Only when she thought of the baby Elizabeth, she was determined nothing should happen to Paul, with his good-natured grin and sparkling brown eyes.

Paul woke up early the next morning, before Ma was stirring or Pa had begun to holler the boys out of bed to do the chores. (Pa was very strict about not sleeping after six o'clock; he said it was a sin to waste the daylight hours snoring.) Lying in bed dreaming while he was awake was one of the pleasantest things a boy could do, Paul thought, and he liked to wake up before the others this way so he could have a little time to "dream." Yesterday Ma had told him a story about a knight (a soldier who wore an iron suit, Ma said) who set out on a white horse in search of the Holy Grail. The story was in one of the poems her master in Kentucky had read, and Ma, who used to sit on a wooden box listening as a child, had remembered the poem word for word in some parts.

Paul wasn't quite sure what the Holy Grail might be, but he pictured himself setting out on a big white horse, and riding, riding, riding . . .

But just as he got to the part where he saw something shining in the distance, he heard Pa's voice from below: "Rob, Buddy! Paul! Git out o' bed, you scamps, it's past six o'clock!"

The two older boys merely grunted and turned over in their cots; and Paul tried to go on with his daydream. But every two minutes Pa was after them, and finally when they heard him say, "Ma, where's my stick?" they tumbled out of their cots and into their overalls, stumbling sleepily down the half-flight of stairs that led into the kitchen. Pa stood at the bottom, looking like a preacher in the frock coat he always wore, and flicked at their legs with the stick.

"Well, you're down. Go along, an' wash at the pump now!" he ordered.

"An' comb your hair while you're there," Ma put in.
"Buddy, don't splatter all over the place."

"That's right, your Ma's got other things to do besides
clean up after you," Pa seconded. He turned to Paul, giving his legs an extra little flick. "Hurry along there, young
'un."

Paul frowned. His legs stung, but he wasn't going to
cry. He wished Pa would stop so he could go on with
his imaginings.

"Don't you dare to frown, boy!" Pa shouted, suddenly
angry. "Straighten up or I'll strap you."

"Let him be, Pa," Ma said quietly, setting a pan of hot
rolls on the table, along with a large granite coffee pot.
"Breakfast is ready now."

"Seems a man can't keep his dignity in his own house,"
Pa muttered, sitting down at the head of the table. "All
right, everybody, fold your hands an' bow your head.
Buddy, take your hands off those rolls till the blessing's
said!" He gave Buddy's knuckles a rap. When everyone's
hands were folded, he began, "Lord, bless this our daily
bread . . . Paul, stop twitchin' your feet."

How could he *see?* Paul wondered. But he held his feet
still until he heard the "Peace-and-joy, Amen" and all the
boys grabbed for a roll. At last breakfast was over, and
Pa left the house to walk downtown, where he joined his
cronies looking for work. He usually stayed away until
long after supper. Sometimes when he came home he
brought a few dollars, but most times he did not, and Ma
had to make out with what she earned. Though he talked
about "making their board and keep" to the boys, he did
mighty little of it; and he thought it was "undignified" for
him to help Ma with the laundry work. The boys could
do that.

And as soon as the breakfast dishes were washed, Ma did

set them all to work. Rob and Buddy had to fill the big
wash tubs with buckets of water from the pump, and chop
enough wood to keep the fire going under the tubs so there
would be plenty of hot water for Ma's wash. When that
was done, they were to deliver the one she had finished last
night.

"What can I do, Ma?" Paul said.

"First you can feed the chickens, manny-boy," Ma told
him, handing him a bagful of crumbs from the bread box,
and adding a fistful of corn. (Ma always kept a few
chickens in the backyard. "If you have a dozen hens, you
can count on having at least half a dozen eggs around,"
she said, though it wasn't always true.)

Paul skipped out to the hen house. He liked to feed the
chickens. The minute he opened the door they came
clustering around, pecking at his bare toes till he reached
into the bag and threw some feed on the ground. Then
they were busy snapping it up; he had to move fast to
keep up with them. Ma had told him not to throw it all
down at once. When the bag was empty, two of the hens
flew up on his arms, poking their beaks inside of it for
more. He laughed and shoved them off. Then he went to
fill the big dipper with water and bring it back to the hen
house for the water pans.

"I'll bring you a drink," he promised. When he went
out, he forgot to latch the door of the coop, and it swung
open; when he came back carrying the dipper, the hens
were trooping out one by one. At first he was going to
shoo them right back inside; but then he wondered what
would happen if they all came outdoors for a change—
chickens must need fresh air, too. He knew Ma never let
them get out, but he swung the door a little wider. Soon
there was a parade of hens marching up the alley. Ma,
glancing from the kitchen door, caught the tail end of it,

and came running toward Paul, followed by the other boys.

"Child, do I see you lettin' those chickens get away?" she demanded.

"I just wanted to air 'em a little," Paul explained.

But Ma was already after her flock, running up to the front of the line and waving her apron wildly. "Shoo, shoo! Get back, you!" she called, but they only scattered in all directions. "Rob, Buddy!" Ma called, and they came to help. Everybody was running a different way.

"Shoo, shoo—get back, you!" Paul sang, dancing around like a demon. He was having the time of his life.

After some time, and a great deal of shooing and clucking, the chickens were safe in the hen house once more, and Ma put the latch on the door herself. "You rascal," she said to Paul. "Next time I'll feed the chickens—no trouble then."

"I'm sorry, Ma," Paul said as they went into the kitchen. "I won't do it again. But didn't we have fun drivin' 'em back?" He and his brothers giggled, remembering how Ma looked.

"Humph," was all Ma said, piling the dirty clothes in the tub.

Later, when Rob and Buddy had gone delivering, Paul asked Ma to finish the story about the knight and the Holy Grail.

"You don't deserve to hear it," she said.

"Please, Ma," he begged. "You tell the best stories in the world."

"You're just a wheedlin' li'l scamp," Ma said. But she told him the story all the same, and soon he was far away, in the poetic land of heroes, and heroic deeds.

CHAPTER II

Pa's Story

Pᴀ ᴄᴏᴜʟᴅ tell stories, too—if he felt like it. His were different as night and day from Ma's. She often told funny tales as well as romantic ones, little bits of plantation life during her childhood that could make you laugh and cry at the same time, or happenings that were such a howl you doubled over with chuckling. But when Pa held forth you were likely to hear about some grim battle during the

war, his hard life on the plantation, or, most interesting
of all, his escape to Canada.

He was usually in a story-telling mood on Sunday afternoons after church, when the dinner dishes were done, and
they sat around in the front room, or on the porch steps
in warm weather, listening to him recall these episodes in
his life. Sometimes it was like listening to the preacher read
an extra chapter from the Bible; sometimes it was spine-
chilling; and always the boys took in every word, solemnly.

Pa had been the plantation plasterer on one of the big
cotton kingdoms in Kentucky, where he was born a slave
many years before. The master, like most plantation
owners, saw to it that the men in jobs like this learned to
read no more than the numbers on the sacks of supplies,
and were taught only enough arithmetic to keep them from
being cheated when they were hired out to neighboring
plantations. Otherwise, no one was allowed a dot of education; slaves were forbidden to look at printed words, much
less find out what they meant.

But somehow someone managed to smuggle an alphabet
into the cabin quarters in a scrapbook. By the light of a
lone candle late at night when everyone else was asleep,
Pa taught himself the ABCs, and how the letters were used
to form different words. Once he had learned to read, he
learned to think—and he knew he must run away, no matter
how great the risk might be. The master had told him he
could buy his freedom if he saved his earnings every time
he was hired out; but Joshua, even with his small knowledge
of arithmetic, could figure out that it would take forever
before the few cents he was paid would add up to fifteen
hundred or two thousand dollars, the price of a slave. Escape was the only way open to him.

The getaway was a dangerous business—if runaway
slaves were caught it meant death or punishment worse

than death—but Pa laid his plans carefully. He found out the name of the nearest neighbor who was connected with the "Underground Railroad," a secret organization that helped slaves escape to freedom before the Civil War. It was started long before the war, as early as 1790, by the Quakers and other people who felt that slavery should be abolished. They joined together to form the Abolition Society, and turned their homes into shelter stations for Negros fleeing northward to Canada.

(In 1831, a slave by the name of Tice Davids escaped from Kentucky and swam across the Ohio River, with his master right after him in a rowboat. Tice waded ashore dripping wet at the village of Ripley, yet there was no trace of him when the master beached the boat a few minutes later. After searching all over, the man said, "He must have gotten away by an underground road." The Abolitionists heard of the remark, and thought it would be a good idea to tie it up with the newly-invented steam railway, so they called their system "The Underground Railroad.") This chain of hiding places formed by people who believed in freedom for slaves was growing longer and longer; it was possible to find refuge right straight through from Kentucky to Canada if you were lucky and knew the ropes.

Pa set off one dark rainy night when the sound of a steady downpour would help to muffle his footsteps, and no one from the mansion would be likely to be outdoors. Two of his friends saw him off, and one of them slipped a box into his hand.

"Th' hot stuff," he whispered. It was cayenne pepper he had swiped from the house, so Pa could sprinkle some in his tracks as he went along. They all knew that bloodhounds would be on his trail as soon as the master discovered he was gone. Cayenne pepper did not always work, but it made the dogs sneeze, and they would lose the scent for a while, anyway.

Pa tried to thank his friend, but the man put a finger to his lips. Then the three silently shook hands, and Pa disappeared into the woods. He was taking a short cut to the nearest town, where he knew a member of the underground was expecting him. From somewhere inside the stables he heard a dog barking, but he plunged into the wet darkness of the woods without stopping.

All night long he plodded through the muddy paths, sure of his way because he had known this part of the forest all his life; and by dawn he had reached the first hideout. He gave the signal—a certain number of raps on the back door—and was let in almost immediately by a man who hurried him down to the cellar. Here he crouched for two days, resting on an old straw mattress in the middle of the floor, and accepting gratefully the warm milk and food the man or his wife would bring down. Around midnight of the second day, when the moon was down and complete darkness covered the Kentucky hills, he went on his way again, with whispered instructions from the man.

At the second place there was one long, terror-filled moment shortly after he arrived, when he heard the baying of the bloodhounds and the thundering of horses' hooves as a posse of plantation owners headed by his master rode up. He listened, horrified, as the voice he knew so well demanded if a runaway had been seen in the neighborhood. But the man upstairs had his story ready, and while Pa listened breathlessly from beneath, he directed the posse to a false trail, saying he'd seen a shadowy figure making for that road the night before.

"Why didn't you stop him?" Pa's master shot out the question.

"Why should I?" the man shrugged. "He wasn't bother-
ing me. I didn't know there were runaways around."

"Well, you know it now," was the curt answer. "If we
don't find him, we'll be back." And the posse rode off.

Pa could not stay at that station more than a couple of
hours, just long enough to give his pursuers a chance to put
a safe distance between them. Then the man of the house
hitched up his wagon, told Pa to lie down in the bottom of
it, and threw a loose bundle of hay on top of him. They
drove off down the right road as fast as they could without
arousing suspicion, and reached the next stop without any
trouble.

Here there were three other runaways already, hiding in
the basement till the "conductor," a member of the underground who did nothing but transport slaves from one
station to another, arrived to take them to the next point to
the north. He had a larger wagon, and could carry as many
as seven at a time, buried under sacks of potatoes or flour.
It was not the most comfortable way to travel, but it was
much faster and safer than going on foot, Pa discovered.
As he made his way farther northward, he saw that the
underground railway was more and more organized; by the
time he reached the Ohio border, crossing the river lying
flat on the deck of a ferry boat late at night, he found the
system had grown into a whole network, spread out on two
main routes and countless by-paths, manned by operators
and conductors, who used a telegraph code—like a regular
railroad. And the runaways were the passengers.

Sometimes they even rode the regular trains, dressed up
in different disguises, a sailor suit for a man, a nurse's uniform for a woman. And always there was someone to take
care of them, to offer food and shelter and lead the way to
freedom.

Of course they still ran risks. Once Pa was hidden in a

secret closet built to look like a chimney and nearly suffo-
cated before he could come out. At the Cherrys, near
Marysville, he and ten others stood quaking with fear in
small concealed cells very cleverly built into the basement,
while a posse searched for them with lighted torches. The
Cherrys' rambling brick house, with its cavernous cellar and
enormous attic sheltered more runaways than any station
of the underground, and none was ever caught. Another
close call came at "Uncle John King's," when a posse unexpectedly pounded at the front door, and Pa found himself
hurried through a two-way tunnel leading from the cellar
to the corn crib and the barn. Three of the six slaves there
at the time went to one place and three to the other, and
the house was empty by the time the men who were after
them got in.

Slowly, station by station, Pa made his way northward
until he reached Sandusky. Here he was put on a boat that
crossed Lake Erie to Detroit, landing on the Canadian side.
He was on free soil, a free man!

He got a job as a plasterer, and managed to make his
living. He could read all he wanted now, but he stuck
mostly to history books. He wanted to find out how the
Africans became slaves in the first place. He also read
the newspapers regularly, watching the struggle between the
North and the South, and when they finally went to war,
he came back to the States to join the colored regiments
that were being formed. He was too late for the first one,
the famous Fifty-fourth Massachusetts, but he enlisted in
the Fifty-fifth, under Colonel Norwood Penrose Hallowell.
How grand the names sounded to Paul's ears—Colonel
Robert Gould Shaw was another Pa told about. He had led
the Fifty-fourth in the battle at Fort Wagner, and died
with his men, all heroes because of their brave charge on
the Fort. And after the battle, one of the soldiers had said

proudly, "The old flag never touched the ground, boys."

Pa was discharged from the Army in 1863, but a couple of months later he re-enlisted, and when the war was over, he was a sergeant. He would pat the sleeve of his coat when he spoke of his rank, and the boys could almost see the stripes that had been on his uniform.

Paul didn't always know what Pa was talking about, but he liked to hear the stories. He wished Pa would tell stories all the time he was around instead of arguing with Ma the way he did. When his parents started to raise their voices in angry words, Paul scurried outdoors with Buddy and Rob, where they would shoot marbles or spin tops behind the hen house until they heard Pa march out on the porch and down the steps, and all was quiet. Then they would come back into the kitchen, where Ma would be ironing, as if nothing had happened.

One day after one of these quarrels, Pa was carrying his carpetbag when he stomped out of the house, and when the boys came in, Ma told them she was getting a divorce. They didn't see Pa much after that. He moved out to the Old Soldiers' Home, where he could do nothing but tell stories all day long if he felt like it. He received a soldier's pension, and sometimes he came to town and took Paul to the circus. Those were happy times, when he and Pa laughed at the clowns, and watched, big-eyed, the acrobats and bareback riders. Then Pa, sitting beside Paul in his frayed frock coat and rusty stovepipe hat did not seem so stern or forbidding.

CHAPTER III

Going-to-School Day

Paul was walking down Howard Street with Buddy and Rob, and he was wearing a new suit, the first of his very own. With a high heart he swung along between his half-brothers in the bright blue September weather. This was the day that had been marked in his mind like a shining hilltop long before he reached it—going-to-school day. He felt as if he were running out into the sky.

Ever since he had been able to talk easily, he had pestered the boys with questions about school: What did they do there? What was the teacher like? Did they read stories in school? And always he wanted to go along. But he was "too little," and he asked too many questions, they said. He'd find out soon enough what school was like!

"When?" Paul would ask Ma. "When can I go, too?"

"As soon as you're six years old," Ma would tell him, but it seemed as if that year would never come.

In the meantime, Ma had taught him the ABCs, so he would be ready for learning. She herself had learned them not so many years before, when she first came to Dayton after the war. Buddy was only two then, and Rob a tiny baby. When Ma saw the children coming home from school past the house every day, she got an idea. She invited them in and gave them cookies, and then she asked them to teach her the letters. As soon as she could pick out a few words, she went to night school for six weeks, where she learned to write as well as read. Here her education had ended, however, because she had to work all the time to support her childen. Still, she could follow the Bible chapters in church now, read the newspapers, and keep her accounts straight, and that meant a great deal to Ma. What was more important, the boys were getting an education; they had the right to receive it.

"You're free to learn as much as you want, child," she had told Paul as she helped him put on the new suit that morning. "You were *born free*—and don't you forget it!"

"I won't, Ma," Paul promised happily; he took the slate and pencil she had bought for him and tucked it under his arm. He was in a hurry to start.

Now he was on the way, actually going to school with Buddy and Rob! From today on, the hours of waiting until they came home to play with him would be over; he would be in school, too. Of course Buddy was in the eighth grade, and Rob in the sixth, but the thought of being even in the first grade gave Paul a delicious sensation, like suddenly being ten feet tall. He took a giant step, and went ahead of his brothers. They had to walk faster to keep up with him.

At the building on East Fifth near Eagle Street—the Fifth District school—they found the playground spilling over with boys and girls, shouting hellos after the long vacation. Buddy and Rob greeted their friends and showed off their little brother. Paul was shy at first—there were so many children, big and little, colored and white, all of them noisy!—but he smiled at everyone, and soon he was jumping off the steps with a bunch of small boys. Then the warning bell rang and they all went inside.

Buddy and Rob took Paul into the first grade, a large room on the ground floor. Here there was a bubbling noise of many children being "still" while the teacher talked with some mothers who had brought their children to school. Paul had time to notice the rows of small desks with benches to fit under them and two girls or boys at each place. The wide window sills were decorated with pots of sweeping ferns lined along the ledge. In one corner at the front of the room stood a blackboard on stilts, and in the other a battered upright piano leaned forward, missing a front caster; the teacher's desk stood in between. When the mothers finally left she turned to the boys.

"William and Robert Murphy," she said with a good-natured smile. "How tall you've grown! What grade are you in now?" She had fat, puffed-out cheeks, and two fat buns of hair wound over her ears.

The boys told her and Buddy said, "This is our half-brother, Paul Dunbar."

"I see." The teacher nodded wisely, still smiling.

And Paul felt bold enough to add, "But my whole name is Paul Laurence Dunbar."

"Well, that's a mighty fine name for a little boy," the teacher laughed. "If you'll just take the first seat in the second row . . ." She pointed to his place, and his brothers, giving him a helping shove toward it, rushed out to their own classrooms before the last bell rang.

Paul found himself next to a boy just his size, who welcomed him with a wink that said plainly, "We'll have some fun together."

Just then the teacher rapped on the desk with a ruler. "Come to order, little people," she said, and although it sounded like "come-to-water" in Paul's ears, he quieted down with the others. But when the boy beside him leaned close and whispered, "How'd you like to stick a pin in those balloon cheeks?" he had to giggle.

The teacher rapped again, more sharply. "Order!" she commanded, and this time there was no mistaking it.

Paul straightened up and sobered his face although he was still shaking inside. But in another moment he was too interested in all that was going on to think about jokes.

First they learned a good-morning song, repeating it line by line after the teacher as she played it on the tinny piano; the words were very simple; he could have sung it by himself the second time around. He sang slightly off-key, but in a strong full voice for a boy his size, and he liked to let it out.

Then, going to the blackboard, the teacher asked, "Did you all bring slates?" adding, "Hold them up so I can see." And Paul, who was still clutching his under his arm, raised it high over his head. When they put them down again, the teacher began to write the alphabet in large letters across the top of the blackboard, using a long stick of chalk. When she finished the row, ending with H, she picked up a wooden pointer and laid it on the A. "Does anyone know what this is?" she asked.

Paul raised his hand and began to rattle off all the letters, fast, the way he did them for Ma. "A-B-C-D-E—"

"Wait a minute!" The teacher laughed. "How many letters do you know?"

"All of 'em," Paul told her.

"The whole alphabet?"

Paul nodded.

"Who taught you?" the teacher asked him.

"My Ma."

The teacher pointed to "H," at the end of the row. "Can you go on from here?"

'Sure." And he began to rattle them off again. "I-J-K-L-M—" He would have gone right on, but the teacher and the whole class started to laugh at the way he was racing. He laughed, too—it did sound funny.

"Not so fast, Paul," the teacher protested. "Say the letters one at a time, and I'll write them on the board."

So he did. Then they all copied a few at a time on their slates until they had gone all the way through to "Z."

Afterward they learned the numbers, from 1 to 10; and, best of all, the teacher read a story to them. When she finished, the children drew pictures about it on their slates. Paul's was not nearly as good as some of the others, but he could have told the whole story to the children if the teacher had asked him. He remembered it without even trying when Ma asked him what he had done at school as soon as he came home with Buddy and Rob. She was anxious to hear everything that happened, but the first thing Paul told her about was the story—to him it was the most important.

School was easy for Paul, all except arithmetic. He had no trouble learning to read or write words, and it was fun to spell them. Every Friday afternoon there was a spell-down, and he usually stayed in till the end. He loved the sound of words that went together, like joy and boy; girl and swirl; faces and places; breeze and freeze—he would skip through the columns in his spelling book and pick out the ones he wanted to put together, jotting down the rhymes he liked best. Nobody knew about this secret game of his—not even Ma, though he told her most things about school. He spent a good part of his time playing with words (often when he should have been working his problems) and one day during his first year he wrote a poem on the inside cover of his spelling book.

Perhaps if he had spent more hours on numbers and less on words, arithmetic wouldn't have been so hard for him; but the figures bored him, and after a few minutes his mind would wander off to more exciting things. Then, too, the family moved several times; he had only been in the Fifth District school two years when Ma decided to take a little cottage on Magnolia Street, near the country fair grounds, and Paul changed to the Third District. The next year they moved to Sycamore Street, and he started at the Tenth District, a Negro school. The following year they were in still a different house, on Scott, a dead-end street beyond the railroad tracks, but luckily it was in the same district, so Paul didn't have to change again. Each time he began at a new school he had to catch on to the different ways the teachers had, and somewhere along the line he missed out on the beginning of fractions so that he never got them straight. After that, he just managed to squeak through in arithmetic, although his report card showed marks of 85 to 100 in everything else.

But no matter where he went to school, Paul made plenty of friends. After he had been at Tenth a while, there was a little gang of boys who went around together, so he never had to beg his brothers to take him along with them any more. (Besides, they began to go with girls, which made them almost grownups.) His best friend was Bud

Burns, an orphan who lived in the neighborhood. Nearly every day Bud would come home with Paul after school and often he stayed for supper when Ma had enough to spare. He seemed to feel at home there, sitting around the kitchen table, and Ma was glad to make him welcome.

Of course he and Paul had their squabbles, like all best friends. Paul was forever beating Bud at marbles; Rob and Buddy had taught him how to shoot, and to keep up with them he had soon mastered the tricks; his aim was dead-sure. He usually gave back the marbles, so Bud wouldn't mind losing, but one day they had played for keeps, and Paul, as always, picked up more than his pockets could hold. He even won the milky blue agate Bud cherished, and when that happened his friend went home crying. But the next day after school Bud started walking home with Paul when the bell rang.

"Let's have a ball game over in the lot," he suggested.

"Sure," Paul said, "only I have to help Ma deliver the wash first. You round up the gang and I'll be there soon's I can."

Bud ran ahead to gather the boys in the vacant lot near the railroad tracks, and Paul hurried home, happy and relieved.

CHAPTER IV

The Littlest Lamplighter

M A HAD quite a few bundles to deliver that afternoon. She and Paul took turns pulling the wooden wagon across the railroad tracks and over the bridge to the better residential section where Ma's customers lived. Rob and Buddy had just found jobs at the livery stables downtown, currying horses after school; and at dusk they were part of a crew of boys who went around lighting the gas lamps. It all helped to bring in enough money so Ma could pay the rent and the boys could stay in school.

Paul and his friends took odd jobs also, to help pay their

way; he and Bud Burns often raked leaves, mowed lawns, or shoveled snow to earn a few pennies; and sometimes, when he delivered the wash with Ma like this, a customer would tip him when he carried the bundle up to the door. But with all their efforts, the coins in Ma's porcelain pig on the kitchen shelf did not amount to enough to cover expenses some weeks. Paul wanted to be a lamplighter, too, and he said so now as they went along Third Street pulling the wagon, but Ma shook her head.

"You're too little," she said from force of habit.

"I'm ten," Paul reminded her. "Rob wasn't any older when he started."

"The boys were always stronger than you, Son," Ma said.

"Oh, Ma!" Paul was disgusted with the old argument.

"But you're a sight smarter," Ma continued, "and that means a lot more in the long run. You get all the book-learning you can."

"But that's why I want to be a lamplighter," Paul was quick to point out.

"Wait a while, manny-boy," Ma said, so he kept still, but his mind was already made up.

Nobody offered him a tip as they made the rounds, and it seemed to take especially long to distribute all the bundles. In some places they had to wait while a pile of dirty laundry was tied up to be dumped in the wagon and hauled home for Ma to do the next day. The sun was setting by the time they crossed the bridge over the Miami River on the way back. The glow made the windows in the row of red brick tenements on the north bank daz-zlingly bright.

"Look, Ma," Paul pointed to the brilliant light. "That's just the way it must've been in the story we read today." He told her about "The House with the Golden Windows" in the McGuffey reader. It had to do with a little boy who used to gaze at the house across the street every day when the sun went down, admiring the panes of glass, and wishing he had some like them. Seeing the fine windows across the street made him sadder and sadder, until one day he met a wise man who told him to get up very early in the morning, cross the street, and look over at his home.

"So he 'arose before the sun was up'," Paul quoted the story, "put on his clothes, and crept out of the house before anyone was awake. He crossed the street as the sun's rays appeared in the sky, turned to look back—and lo'n'-behold, his own house was the one with the golden windows!" He finished with a flourish of his hand, letting go of the wagon.

They had come to the far side of the bridge, where it sloped down to the road; Ma had been listening so intently she forgot the wagon, too, and it rolled toward the railing, ready to plunge over the side.

"Paul!" Ma gasped.

But he was ahead of her and grabbed hold of the handle just in time. One of the bundles was about to topple into the water, but Ma caught it, and they halted the wagon.

"Boy, the Wrights' laundry almost got washed in the river!" Paul laughed.

Ma laughed, too. "You're better 'n the Bijou, Son—a regular show all by yourself, with your stories and jokes."

They hurried the rest of the way, because Paul wanted to get back before the ball game was over. But when he reached the vacant lot, Bud was there by himself, trying to untangle the strings of a large kite from the telephone wires overhead. He and Paul had made the kite together out of newspaper and thin scraps of wood from the lumber yard and some flour-and-water paste Ma fixed for them.

"Doggone wires," Bud said as Paul came up. "Wish

people wouldn't be so quick to put telephones in—you can't even get a kite up any more with wires all over."

Paul agreed; the first phones in Dayton had been installed only a few years before, and already wires were stretched across most of the town. Everybody who could possibly afford it wanted to try out the new invention.

"What happened to the game?" Paul asked, trying to help Bud with the kite.

"Couldn't find anybody," Bud said briefly, struggling with the strings. "They all had jobs—and I went around to rake leaves for Captain Stivers 'fore I came here." (The Captain, Principal of Central High, often gave the boys work.) After a few minutes, Bud threw down the bolt of thread. "Let's leave the old kite; maybe the wind'll blow it down."

Paul was more than willing. The boys ambled over to the river bank and began skipping stones across the water. Some of them sank with a noisy splash, and Paul liked to watch the circles on the surface widen out farther and farther.

"Jake Payne's brother is quitting school," Bud said, watching the ripples. "Says he can get a job down at the Beckel Hotel."

"Buddy and Rob are talking about it, too," Paul told him.

"Are you going to quit next year?" Bud asked.

"Not if I don't have to!" Paul picked up a stone and threw it hard across the water. "How about you?"

"Same here," Bud nodded. "Depends on how many jobs we can get, I s'pose."

Most of the pupils at Tenth had the same problem, and a great many left school at the sixth or seventh grade, because their families needed the money they could earn at full-time jobs. This was true in other schools also; in fact, there were so few eighth graders in Dayton that they were all in one school, the Intermediate, on Brown Street. Even less were able to go on to high school, and graduating classes numbered only a handful, twenty or thirty students.

"Say!" Paul's face brightened suddenly. "If Will and Rob do get in down at the Beckel, maybe we can take their places as lamplighters!"

"Man, you're talking! Let's ask 'em soon's they come home!" Bud grabbed Paul's arm, and they ran back to Ma's.

When the older boys heard of the plan, they agreed to do what they could, and Ma was satisfied because it meant that Paul would "wait a while," as she had suggested.

In the spring Buddy, who completed his first year in high school, decided he had had enough education, and applied for a job at the Beckel House. Rob, just graduating from the eighth grade, followed suit; and Paul and Bud became lamplighters. They were each put in charge of a certain number of blocks on the west side of town, close to home.

Paul had grown some in height, but he was still skinny, and the smallest of the crew setting out the first night. When he and Bud called "good luck" to each other as they separated, he wondered if his friend felt as jumpy inside as he did. He shifted the ladder on his shoulder, took a firm grip on the torch, and made for the nearest post, on the corner of Wilkinson and Tenth. He hoped he could do everything the way the supervisor had shown them.

He had to hoist the ladder high over his head to hook it on the crosspiece of the lamp post; he tried three times before it was safely fixed in place. Then he lit the torch, and jumped up to the lowest rung of the ladder. He climbed slowly, because it swayed slightly, and he didn't care to lose his balance or drop the torch. There were not many steps (the posts weren't very tall), but the way seemed long, and his legs shook a little by the time he reached the top. He stood perfectly still for a moment or two, steadying himself, checking the lamp to be sure of the next thing he had to do.

Yes, there was the gas cock. He pushed the torch under it, and turned on the gas. Ooh, what a smell! He hadn't been prepared for the fumes that filled his nostrils till he could scarcely breathe; he sputtered and choked and coughed so hard he almost fell off the ladder. But in a second the flame leaped up and burnt off the gas and the air cleared. He sucked it in and smiled. Why, that was easy! The globe was shining with light, and so were Paul's eyes. He clambered down and fairly capered along the street to the second corner.

This time it was easier because he knew what he was doing. When he turned on the gas he held his breath till the flare was going strong so the fumes didn't bother him nearly as much. By the third lighting, he was up the rungs in a trice, lit the lamp, and ran down again in less time than it had taken him to hook the ladder onto the crosspiece in the beginning.

At the bottom, just as he was about to hurry on to the next corner, he saw a little girl looking out of the window, watching him. He smiled and waved to her, and she waved back delightedly, as if she had been waiting for him to notice her. Oh, this job was going to be fun. He sped along the streets, going from one post to another like an old-timer.

He finished in his "territory" earlier than some of the other boys. Before starting for the station, he looked back at the gleaming lamps, and felt as if he had pulled down a handful of stars to light up the darkness of the earth.

All that year Paul and Bud Burns were lamplighters. Paul became so skillful he could do the job in half the time it took at first, if he scurried from one lamp post to another without stopping. But sometimes he spent a few minutes talking to the little girl who had waved to him, or to his schoolmates, if they happened to pass by in the block he was working on at the moment. Sometimes on Third Street, men getting off the horse-car on the way home from the office would stand watching him light the lamp; and when he climbed down they would ask him questions about the job and how such a youngster could manage it. And sometimes, at the last post, Paul would stay up at the top, dreaming beside the yellow-blue flame in spite of the faint odor of gas that lingered in the air.

He was always reading stories and poems, and pictures of them would drift before his eyes in the flickering light. Or he would begin making up something of his own, and completely forget to come down until he felt cramped or had a sudden urge to put his thoughts down on the blue-lined tablet paper at home. Then he would scramble from the ladder, report at the station, and rush home without waiting for Bud. He was always scribbling, and Ma encouraged him; she took it for granted he was doing his lessons. Most of the time he wasn't, but he let her think so; if Ma thought he was studying, he didn't have to do chores, and Paul hated chores more than anything. The woodbox always needed filling, and so did the wash tubs, or else they needed emptying; there was never an end to chores. If Paul was deep in a book, or busy writing, Ma would tell one of the older boys to do the job at hand and make no fuss about it.

During the winter, people in Dayton began talking about electricity. The *Herald* hinted, in an article which set everybody buzzing, that before too long the whole town would be lit by electric street lights.

"It's just a rumor," some said. "How can some kind of current in the air light up a city?"

"Look at the telephone," said others. "It certainly has caught on, and it works by electricity."

Still others shook their heads as they tied their horses to the hitching posts downtown, and "wondered what the world was coming to."

Paul and his friends didn't pay too much attention to the talk. None of their families had telephones yet—Ma could afford no such luxury, nor could most of the others—and the possibility of electric street lights seemed very remote. Bud and Paul continued to make their rounds with ladder and torch each evening at twilight.

But one day in late spring as the two were coming home from school, they noticed a crew of workmen and horses excavating the ground in the commons near Paul's house. A line of curious spectators stood along the edge taking in the operation—men and a few women as well as school children were looking on with great interest.

Paul approached a friend of his. "Hey, Ennis! What's going on here? Or is it going up?"

Ennis laughed. "Right the second time. You know what they're fixin' to do, Paul?"

"What?"

"Set up dynamos for the 'lectric lights."

Paul's eyes grew big. "You're spoofing!"

"No, I'm not. Ask the foreman. Ask Mr. Finley over there." He nodded toward a man they both knew standing in line close by.

It was true. Two huge dynamos were to be set up on the commons, and the power would be furnished by a saw-mill. Not all of Dayton would be "electrified," but a good portion would; and later more dynamos would be set up so electric street lights would extend from one end of town to the other. "Biggest thing that ever hit Dayton," Mr. Finley told the boys.

But as Paul and Bud walked away they did not feel so cheery. The coming of electric street lights meant one job less for the boys to rely on. Within the year, all of Dayton gaped and blinked in the blaze of light along its streets; and Paul and Bud were no longer lamplighters.

CHAPTER V

Ma's Story

Now THE old question raised its snarling head—could they manage things so Paul wouldn't have to quit school? It was true that education was free, but the clothes and school supplies he needed were expensive for Ma. Her oldest son was engaged, and would soon be on his own.

"Buddy's got a girl, Buddy's got a girl!" Paul teased him.

"*Will*," corrected his brother, who didn't like to be called by the old nickname now that he was almost twenty; but he was smiling. "Sure, I've got a girl, and I'm going to marry her. What's wrong with that, Smartie?"

"Ugh!" Paul made a face. He wrote a jingle and handed it around the table one night. Called "A Meeting with an Old Friend," it began,

> Hello, old friend, are you married?
> No, I'd just as soon be buried!

and ended,

> Take your matrimony with you.
> To me it's thin as tissue.

Everybody laughed, including Will, who tweaked Paul's ear.

"Wait till you're my age, Smartie!"

"When I'm twenty I'll do more than get married," Paul bragged breezily, and his brothers roared.

But earning a living was no laughing matter, and they had to settle down to facts. After Will and his "girl" Meta were married, Rob decided to try his luck somewhere else. He was tired of sweeping out floors at the Beckel House, and there were rumors that business was going from bad to worse in Dayton. He began to talk about going to Cincinnati, the sprawling river town on the bank of the Ohio, where jobs were supposed to be more plentiful. And a few weeks later he asked Ma to get his clothes ready so he could leave.

After Rob had gone, Paul and Ma had to manage the household by themselves. Along about this time, Joshua Dunbar died, and Paul applied for his share of his father's pension, but so far nothing had come of it. (Pa had been half sick for several years; occasionally, on Sunday afternoons, Paul had walked five miles out to the Old Soldiers' Home to visit him, but for a long time Pa had not come to town.)

Ready to try anything, Paul went down to the Beckel House to see if he could take over Rob's old job for a couple of hours after school; but they wanted only full-time workers, the man told him. He hung around outside the hotel when he left the office; perhaps he could find a job running errands for one of the traveling men who were lounging in the rockers on the porch. But all he heard was gloomy business talk about poor sales, and the possibility of a panic in New York or Philadelphia.

He crossed the street and went down the block to the other hotel; here things were livelier. A man wearing a flowered waistcoat with a large gold watch-chain across the front of it sprang out of his carriage, and asked Paul to hold the horses a few minutes while he went into the hotel on business.

"Sure, Mister." Paul took the reins and hung on till the man came out. He had not been long and he handed Paul a nickel before getting back into the carriage. If there had been a few more like him, Paul would have had a profitable afternoon; but even so, Ma was glad to add the nickel to the small pile of change in the porcelain pig. "Every penny counts, Son," she said, slipping it into the slot. "We'll make it yet." Hearing her voice, so full of confidence, Paul was sure they would.

For supper, they had chitt'lins and cottage-fried potatoes. And of course, a pan of cornpone, which Ma pulled from the oven, piping hot, just before they sat down. Paul thought perhaps the nicest moment of the day came at supper time, when Ma set the cornpone on the table, and the warm, delicious aroma filled his nostrils all during the blessing. Things had a way of smoothing out when Ma said the blessing and the cornpone was hot in front of them.

After supper, Paul did the dishes while Ma dampened the clean clothes she had just taken off the backyard lines, and got the irons out for the night's work. When he finished, Paul prepared for his work, too—lessons. He hated arithmetic, but the problems had to be done, if he wanted to stay in school. For a while his head was bent over the blue-lined tablet, and he bit his lower lip, concentrating. Then he lost interest, as usual, and his mind wandered.

"Ma," he asked, looking up suddenly, "How'd you happen to come to Dayton?"

"I s'pect because my mammy was here," Ma shook the ruffle on a shirtwaist. "Why?"

"Oh, I was just wondering," Paul said. "How'd she get here?"

"Well, it's kind of a long story," Ma began, and Paul slyly slipped his tablet and pencil into the arithmetic book and closed it. He settled down in the carpet-back rocker to listen.

Ma still used the same opening she had when he was small. "Once upon a time . . ."

"When you were a little girl in Kentucky," Paul smiled.

But Ma shook her head. "No, long before I was a little girl." She puckered her forehead into a deep frown. It all started, she said, with Aunt Becca Porter, Paul's great-grandmother. She had been a slave in Fayette County, Kentucky, living in a cabin quarters on a large plantation, like thousands of others. But through sheer good fortune, she was bought by a man from the north, a Mr. Samuel Steele, of Dayton, who was shocked at the way slaves were treated, as if they were cattle instead of human beings. He hated the sight of the auction block, where slaves were sold. To set an example for others, he made up his mind to buy a slave for freedom instead of bondage. He bought Aunt Becca Porter, took her back up north to Dayton, saw to it that she had a place to live and a job, and then he set her free.

Somehow, word of Aunt Becca's miraculous luck traveled down to Kentucky: the story spread through the cabin quarters of one plantation after another until it reached the unbelieving ears of Matilda and her mother, Liza. One of their own kin was free! It was hard for them to picture what Dayton must be like, but one thing they both resolved was that they would see it for themselves some day. Although Matilda was only a child, she vowed to herself that she would escape to a free land when she grew up.

"Well, the years passed by, and my Mammy got her freedom, too," Ma continued sarcastically, "only twa'nt any present, I can tell you." She banged the irons on the stove, changing handles.

"Why? What happened?" Paul was sitting forward in the rocking chair now, intent on hearing the story.

"She got too old to work," Ma explained. "Or at least her master thought she was too old to be much use on the plantation any more, so he set her free—free to starve, for all he knew, but that never bothered a slave owner. He just wanted to get out o' carin' for slaves who couldn't break their backs for him any more.

"My mammy made her way to Dayton—I b'lieve Mrs. Steele sent her some money. And when she came to the station, that blessed lady was waiting for her, and took her to old Aunt Becca. Later on, she found a job, too!" Ma finished defiantly.

"How come you didn't go with her?" Paul asked.

"I still had plenty of work in my bones," Ma said. "I can't even remember which place I was at when she came to see me before she left."

Ma's story was different from that of most slaves. She was "hired out" at the age of seven, and from then on she went from place to place until she was nineteen, when Emancipation came. She had been born on the plantation of Squire David Glass. When she was about four years old, her master was taken seriously ill, and one of the earliest tasks she could remember was pulling the rope of the big fan suspended from the ceiling, which brushed the flies from his face.

The Squire died, and the farm was broken up. Ma and her mammy were taken to the home of Mr. Glass's married daughter, the Venables, in Lexington, Kentucky. After a short while she was separated from her mother, and sent to Colonel White's, in Louisville. The Colonel was another son-in-law of Squire Glass, so she was still owned by the same family, and although the Colonel hired her to different people from the time she was seven, he remained her master. At first she was so lonesome for her mother she wouldn't eat, but she gradually became used to being on her own, fending for herself wherever she was working. She had often told Paul the comic side of her experiences, like the time she was hired out to the stingiest woman in Fayette County.

The old lady was so tight she would rather let the apples that fell on the ground rot underneath the tree than give them to anybody. Matilda, who was about fourteen and always underfed, used to snatch one up and sneak behind the barn to eat it. One day, when she was going to fetch water from the pump, balancing the bucket on her head, she passed the carriage boy, who was polishing the lamps on their mistress's ancient buggy. "Psst," he hissed, "bring me a couple of apples on the way back, will you, Till?" They were right outside the parlor windows, and the mistress was entertaining guests, so Matilda merely nodded and walked straight on. She filled the pail with water, grabbed a few apples from the ground and slung them into the pail where they bobbed up and down. Then she hoisted the bucket to her head and started back toward the house. Reaching the spot where the boy was, she threw the apples onto the carriage floor as fast as she could get hold of them, and went on.

But right at that moment, the mistress happened to look out of the window; she saw the apples going into the carriage, and drew her own conclusions. Leaving her guests, she ran out of the house and called, "Till, come back here!" But Matilda kept right on walking, as if she hadn't heard. The mistress came after her. "Matilda, stop, I say!" Ma only walked faster, and the old lady hurried along beside her. "I saw you throw 'Lishe those apples," she said accusingly. "What have you got there—a whole bucketful?" Some imp made Ma keep going, her lips tightly closed. In a rage, the old lady reached up and seized the rim of the pail, and all the water spilled down upon her! Matilda ran off behind the barn, frightened but giggling with uncontrollable mirth, and her mistress returned to her visitors, drenched to the waist.

"She was looking for apples, but she got a showerful of water in her face," Ma used to end the story, while Paul went off into gales of laughter. She didn't tell him that she had received a whipping the next morning for her prank. As a slave she suffered so many whippings anyhow, one more or less didn't matter. And she didn't want Paul to see too much of the unhappy side of her days in slavery. He had heard enough of that from Pa when he was little.

But she thought he was old enough now to know how she had loathed being a slave, even though she made the best of it, and tried to look back on the brighter moments. She was ready to risk anything to get away from it when liberation came.

"If freedom hadn't come, Boy, I might've been killed," she said, holding the flatiron up dramatically in mid-air.

"Tell me, Ma." Paul was all ears.

So she continued the story. The next place she had gone, at the age of sixteen, proved to be an important one in her life, because there she had met and married Willis, the

Murphys' handyman. (After the war, she and Willis took
the master's last name for their own.) It was a harsh, op-
pressive existence, even with the relief brought by revival
meetings, occasional parties, or "break-downs," as the
dances were called (" 'cause everybody was broken down
from dancin' by the time dawn came," Ma explained). She
had to milk a dozen cows before she started the day's house-
work. One of the herd was ornery as a mule; she balked
and kicked when Ma tried to milk her; but when Ma,
frightened, went crying to the mistress, she was threatened
with a whipping if she didn't "milk that cow, no matter
what. . . ."

When it was time for Ma's baby to be born, she was sent
back to her owner, Colonel White. Nobody asked whether
she minded leaving her husband; nobody cared. And Willis
dared not leave the Murphys, who owned him; if he tried,
he would be a runaway. After Buddy was born—on Lincoln's birthday, February 12, 1862—Ma and the baby were
sent to the first household she had worked in, the Time-
wells. Mr. Timewell had died, but her old mistress was the
same—not cruel, like so many of them, but cold and distant.
She did take the baby into the big house, and cared for him
there, so Matilda would have more time to work. But it was
heavy work and long hours, and Matilda wanted to be with
Willis.

"The worst part of slavery, Son," Ma said, "is that a
body didn't have the say over his own life."

Then she had heard about Negroes going to Liberia; she
had listened behind the curtains to the talk about a free life
there—one of Mrs. Timewell's guests had been promoting
the return of American slaves to Africa as a means of solv-
ing the problem and avoiding a civil war. Ma listened carefully to what the man said about the Negroes signing up
at the Courthouse in Shelbyville, and there in the darkness

she made up her mind to try for a free life, even if it meant crossing the ocean.

The next day, when Mrs. Timewell went away on an overnight visit to relatives, Ma got dressed in her best calico, bundled up the three-month-old Buddy, and set off on foot for Aunt Doshy's cabin. It was five miles along a back-country road, and she had to climb fences carrying the baby in her arms; how she did it, she never knew, but she was finally knocking on Aunt Doshy's door. Leaving the baby there, she borrowed an old nag from the people in the next cabin, and rode seven miles to Shelbyville. At the Courthouse, with trembling fingers, she made an "X" below the line on which the man wrote her name, signing her up to sail for Africa on a ship leaving in six months. When Willis came to see her on his next day off (slaves were permitted to visit their families once in a while, if they were willing to hike ten miles or more each way), she would tell him what she had done, and he could sign up.

On the way home, Ma was full of doubt over her sudden decision. She was filled with terror at the thought of crossing the ocean to a strange land; and who could tell what Liberia was like?

"But freedom came before it was time for me to go," she said with a wide smile, seeing Paul's eyes, so solemn and concerned.

She was working at Dr. Cary's, in Louisville, when Emancipation came. Mrs. Timewell decided to stay with her relatives, and so Matilda was hired out once again. This household was a pleasant one; the doctor had two nieces, Alice and Phoebe Cary, who were poets; they had had books published, which placed them among the immortals in Ma's eyes. Here she heard poetry again, and grew to know and understand it more. But slavery was slavery; and when the Emancipation Proclamation was an-

nounced, she sang "Hallelujah" and jumped for joy with
the other servants in the kitchen at Dr. Cary's.

Soon afterward Willis had joined her, and for a few
months they were together. Then, like Joshua Dunbar,
Willis felt that he should share in the battle to make their
freedom secure. He gave Matilda a watch, his only pos-
session, and told her she should try to get to Dayton, where
she could stay with her mother. He would meet her there
when the war was over.

Matilda sold the watch to get money for her fare, but
she had no idea how to make the journey to Ohio. The
only way she had ever traveled was on foot or horseback.
Then a man in the boardinghouse offered to show her the
way, if she would wait "till day after to-morrow." She
stayed, and he was as good as his word. He worked for
a steamboat company that made trips between Louisville
and Cincinnati. He saw to buying her tickets on the boat
and at the railroad station in Cincinnati; he took care of her
baggage, and helped her with the baby.

"And that's how I came to Dayton," Ma finished the
story. "I found my mammy, and we lived in that house
on Howard Street where you were born. I still had to
work, sure, but I was free to work the way I wanted, to
keep my babies with me, and care for 'em; to get a little
book-learnin', and see that they got some . . ." Here she
broke off and looked squarely at Paul. "Say, did you finish
your 'rithmetic?" She knew his trouble with the subject
only too well.

Paul opened his arithmetic book quickly. "I—uh,uh, just
have a couple more problems to do, Ma."

She gave him a sidelong glance. "Boy, how did I let you
bamboozle me like that?"

They both burst out laughing.

CHAPTER VI

A New School and a New World

THE NEXT YEAR, a few weeks before he was thirteen, Paul passed from district school to Intermediate; and in the fall one Monday morning he cut across the sea of yellow goldenrod in the vacant lot, up over the railroad tracks, heading for Brown Street. It seemed strange to be going to school in a new direction, without Bud Burns, or Charley Higgins, another close friend he had made during the past year. Bud and Charley were both a little younger than Paul, and would be at Tenth one more term.

He wondered who his classmates would be. Since all eighth graders were in one building, there would be a sprinkling of students from every school in town. His cousin, Dora Burton, whose family lived on the East Side, had gone to Intermediate the year before; she was at Central High now. For a fleeting moment, as he went up the

steps, Paul wished she were still in the eighth grade, so he
would be sure of seeing at least one familiar face. And as
he entered the classroom for pupils from Tenth, he looked
around for some of the boys and girls who had been promoted with him, but none was there; they must all have
had to quit school.

He handed his promotion card to the principal, Professor
Wilson, who nodded in a friendly way, and assigned him
to a seat. Across the aisle sat a boy Paul knew slightly—
Orville Wright, whose father, Reverend Wright, had performed the ceremony when Ma and Pa were married. The
Wrights were Ma's customers; and Paul had often seen
Orville or his older brother, Wilbur, when he helped Ma
deliver the wash, but he had never had time to become
acquainted with the boys.

"Hello, Paul." Orville grinned at him as if they were old
friends, his blue eyes twinkling. His blond hair was slicked
back for school, but the lock next to the part stood upright,
as always.

"Hello, Orville," Paul smiled back, glad to find someone
he knew.

"That's Ezra Kuhns on the other side of you," Orville
said in a quick whisper, noticing that the professor was
about to call the class to order. "This is Paul Dunbar, Ez."

Paul just had time to turn toward the large stocky boy
on the left, whose small sharp eyes peered at him from behind thick gold-rimmed glasses, when the Principal rapped
for "attention." The two boys shook hands and nodded;
and Paul took a second or two studying Ezra's spectacles.
Very few people could afford eyeglasses and they were
worn mostly by old folks, seldom by children. But he
didn't want to stare and make Ezra feel funny. And Mr.
Wilson was speaking.

He explained that as Principal he taught one subject—

English, including literature and composition. They would have other teachers for mathematics, history, and science. This would be their study or home room. He added that, if any boys were interested, he would instruct a class in football after school.

A murmur of excitement went over the room. Football— that was a college game! Harvard and Yale played football, but nobody ever heard of a high school team, let alone an intermediate one. Several of the boys whistled and the girls tittered at the unusual announcement.

Professor Wilson's pale scholarly face bore a suggestion of a smile, but he merely repeated firmly, "After school," with the emphasis on the first word. He went on to say that since this was opening day they would not have regular classes, but go through the schedule to get assignments, books, etc., from the teachers. During this first hour, ordinarily a study hour, he would read to them. He was a poet himself, though he hadn't had much published; but he was going to read the work of a famous poet, Tennyson's *Idylls of the King*.

Paul sat forward in his seat. He never expected to have a teacher like Professor Wilson, who was both football player and poet. A perfect combination so far as thirteen-year-old Paul was concerned! He listend closely to the rhythmic cadence of the lines, and suddenly made a startling discovery: this was the way words sang inside of him sometimes, only they didn't always come out so superbly tuned; but the feeling was there. It was the same kind of singing!

Then all at once, as the reading continued, Paul pictured Ma, standing over the ironing board in the kitchen, and he made another discovery: here was the story of the knight and the Holy Grail, which she had told him so many times. One of Ma's stories, in Tennyson's *Idylls of the King* . . .

When school let out at noon, he hurried home to tell her all about Intermediate.

"I'm back, Ma," he called, letting the front door bang behind him as he went through the house. But Ma was out in the yard, taking in the wash.

"I'll be there in a minute," she called. "You'll find corn-pone in the kitchen safe, and there's a pot o' soup on the stove."

Paul went out to help her carry in the basket of laundry, and then over lunch he told her about the new school, especially about Mr. Wilson, the football instruction—and the poetry.

Ma was a good listener and she lapped up every word of Paul's report, but when he finished there was still something she wanted to hear. "You didn't mention anybody you knew at school 'cept the Wrights' boy, Orville," she said. "Weren't there some others from Tenth in your class?"

"Nope, not a one," Paul said. "I thought two or three would be going on to Intermediate, but they must've quit."

"Any colored children from other schools in your class?" Ma went on to ask.

"Why, no, I guess I'm the only one!" Paul said in some surprise. Until this moment he hadn't realized he was the only Negro in Room 10; nobody stared at him even briefly, the way he had gaped at Ezra Kuhn's eyeglasses. They were all new at Intermediate, and Paul Dunbar was just another member of the class.

He became much more than that as the weeks went by. He was a good student—except for mathematics—and the teachers began to take notice of his work in composition. He was not a brilliant scholar but he had an earnest desire to learn, an eagerness to read the great thoughts of men; and he had a quality which distinguished him. He had a way with words, written or spoken; and he had a way with

people, young or old, colored or white. Ma, listening to
the accounts of school he gave Bud and Charley, who came
over from Tenth nearly every afternoon, waited for some
incident of race prejudice or anti-Negro feeling against
Paul, but none took place.

The younger boys heard so much about Intermediate
they felt as if they were in Paul's class. They knew how
smart Orville Wright was in science, and how Ezra Kuhns
could beat almost anybody in the weekly debates—except
Paul, who was learning from him, and sometimes matched
him point for point. (Ezra would argue tooth and nail
during a debate, but he never got sore; whether he won or
lost, he was always good-natured when it was over, and
gave Paul hints on debating for the next contest.) When
Paul showed his two friends how Professor Wilson had
taught the boys to pass and tackle, they were ready to form
a West Side football team. And when Paul had to recite
a piece at the regular Friday afternoon Assembly in the
auditorium, Bud and Charley listened patiently while he
rehearsed until they knew every line, gesture and inflection
almost as well as he, although neither of them could have
performed the way he could.

Paul's readings at Assembly soon became very popular
with the students. He gave a poem life and drama, instead
of reading it off the paper sing-song like most of the pupils.
He won the nickname of "Deacon Dunbar" for his dignity
and poise. Once after Paul had recited a poem about a
shipwreck, Orville Wright came up to him as they were
filing out of the auditorium.

"You sure made that shipwreck real, Deac," he said with
open admiration.

"Thanks, Orville," Paul's face lit up; Orville had pushed
through two lines of students just to give him a word of
praise.

"When those waves washed over the deck and the old ship started to crack, I thought I was drowning myself," Orville went on. And several of the boys around them who heard his remark chimed in, "So did I." "That's right." "You bet!"

"Aw, cut it out," Paul said; but he was tickled.

A few weeks later Professor Wilson told the class that instead of the usual Friday composition, anyone who wanted to try writing a poem could do so for the next assignment. He suggested taking the work of a master, like Shelley's "Clouds," which he had just finished reading to them, and using it as model. "Copy the form of the poem you choose," he said; "the same number of lines, rhythm, and meter; make the same lines rhyme. That way you will learn to write good verse from the beginning. The thoughts, of course, must be your own," he added.

Paul listened carefully. He had been scribbling stanzas in a small notebook for a long time, but it never occurred to him to pattern his poems on those famous authors. He would try it. He would pick one of his favorites—Keats, maybe; "Ode on a Grecian Urn."

That Sunday he and Ma were walking slowly home from church, sniffing the first hints of spring in the air, when Paul got an idea for his poem. It was near Easter, and Reverend Butler had preached a sermon on the meaning of Lent and the holy season. Paul had never before realized how much more Easter meant than bright-colored eggs and altar lilies and new shoes (if Ma could afford them). In the Bible story, Christ had died, and people went to the grave to mourn him . . .

Ma, who was humming "Swing Low, Sweet Chariot," stopped suddenly as they neared the house, and sniffed the air sharply, detecting a smell far from fragrant. "Child, that's my dinner!" She left him on the run for the door, and when Paul reached the kitchen she was standing with the blackened pots in her hand. She was disgusted. "Serves me right for pokin' along in the spring sunshine!"

Paul chuckled. Ma always put her boiled dinner on the stove before they left for church on Sundays, and sometimes it was more than done by the time they returned. Today she would have to start all over.

"Think you can wait, Son?" she asked.

"Sure, Ma, I'll do my lessons," Paul told her.

"Worst trouble is I'll have to use tomorrow's food," Ma added in some distress.

But Paul didn't hear her. He was already leafing through his literature book to find the poem he wanted. Getting out his tablet and pencil, he set to work, counting the lines in the poem, the number of words to the line, and the number of syllables in the words. Then he began patterning his own poem after the one in front of him.

> To the cold dark grave they go,
> Silently and sad and slow,

he wrote. It didn't occur to him that Professor Wilson's formula was a poor one to follow if he was going to be a true poet. He was too new at writing to realize that such a method would give him a copycat style like most poets' in 1885. He was so busy putting down lines, crossing them out, or changing words to match the rhythm of the printed ones in front of him that even when the food was done he kept Ma waiting until she said, "I can't hold back dinner forever, Son."

Yet when Professor Wilson handed back the papers the next week, he asked Paul to remain a few minutes after class. Paul wondered, as he stood by the desk watching the others file out, what the teacher was going to say, but he was not prepared for the praise he received.

"Your poem, 'An Easter Ode,' is an amazingly good piece of work, Paul," Mr. Wilson began; "it has a depth of thought and feeling that is most unusual in a beginner."

Inside Paul was shouting "Hallelujah!" in jubilant tones, but he said calmly, "Thanks, Mr. Wilson." His eyes were shining.

"I have been noticing your compositions," the professor continued, "and some of them have been remarkable, but this shows real talent. I hope you will go on writing poetry in high school. You are going to Central next year, aren't you?" he asked.

"If I possibly can," Paul said, adding suddenly, "And I mean to go on writing poetry the rest of my life!"

Mr. Wilson laughed. "You keep that spirit," he said. "You'll have some good teachers at Central who will help you, I'm sure. But if you ever want to come back here, I'll be glad to go over your poems with you."

Paul thanked him again and left with his paper, his feet scarcely touching the floor as he went down the steps two at a time. Once outside the building, he raced home to tell Ma. She was hanging out clothes when he came running up and grabbed her by the waist, whirling her around the backyard.

"Land o' Goshen, what's got into you?" she sputtered when she could catch her breath.

So Paul told her, helping her with the wash. Back in the kitchen, Ma plumped down in the carpet-back rocker, a thing she seldom did, while Paul put away the empty baskets. Then he took the paper out of his pocket and uncreased it. "You want to hear my poem, Ma?"

"That's what I'm waiting for, Son, and you know it," she said.

He smoothed the paper and began to read in his deep, clear voice. As she listened, Ma began to rock back and forth slowly, but at the end she sat quite still for a long moment, her hands folded in her lap, her eyes brimming over.

"Just beautiful," she murmured. "Like a sermon; only better than a sermon." She had the feeling that somehow Pa's words at Paul's birth were going to come true. "Paul, I think you ought to show your poem to Reverend Butler tonight at Meeting."

"All right, Ma," Paul nodded. "I'm glad you like it so much." He was going to prayer meeting with Bud and Charley; there was to be a taffy pull at the parish house later, and the boys wanted to get in on the fun. As soon as supper was over, Paul scrubbed his face, brushed his hair carefully, and was ready before they came to pick him up. "I have to see the preacher tonight," he explained as the three started out.

Reverend Butler was so impressed with Paul's poem, he suggested putting it on the Easter program, in which the older children took part—reading from the Bible or reciting a religious piece.

On Easter morning Paul sat in the front pews with the other children on the program, waiting for his turn; Ma had managed to buy him a new pair of shoes, which pinched his toes, but he hardly noticed it. The sun streaming through the windows made a prism of color on the two Easter lily plants, and the wheezy old organ swelled out the tunes of spirituals enough to split the rafters of the church.

At last it was time for Paul to recite his poem. As he mounted the three steps to the altar his heart was pounding, but his voice in the opening words was strong and steady, and the congregation sat up and paid attention. That Dunbar boy was a natural-born preacher—and a writer, too! Ma, seeing their faces, felt her heart swell with pride, and she offered up a prayer of her own—a prayer of thanksgiving.

Paul could hear her voice during the closing hymn, blending with the organ, and rising above it. When Ma opened up her throat in song, the tones soared out in golden waves that reached clear to Heaven; and today they were doubly pure and bright.

On the way out of church, people stopped them to praise Paul and congratulate Ma. Bud and Charley and some of the girls came running up to Paul. Everybody stood around in groups, talking about the Easter program; the sun was warm on their backs, and overhead the maple trees in bloom showered the air with spring fragrance. Nobody gave a thought to going home.

It was long past noon when Ma and Paul reached the corner near their house, and Ma, suddenly remembering dinner, hustled him on. She had built only a small fire in the stove before they left, but she had not expected to stay at church so late. "Oh, my beautiful Easter ham! It's sure to be burnt black by this hour," she predicted as they took off. She had saved the "meat-money" all during Lent to buy it; and though Paul called out to her, "There's no smoke," she rushed ahead.

But when he came into the kitchen, her face was beaming. "The fire's plumb gone out!" she announced happily.

"Looks like the Lord held back dinner for us, Ma," he grinned. They hugged each other.

CHAPTER VII

Central High

ALL THROUGH the summer Paul and his friends worked at the same old odd jobs around Dayton homes and hotels, trying to earn enough for school when autumn came. Paul would need extra funds this year, because in high school books had to be bought, as well as other supplies. He had graduated from Intermediate, but could he go on? It was always a question.

Saturday afternoons the boys took their bamboo poles down by the Dayton View bridge, and sometimes they caught enough catfish, yellow-bellies, and bullheads to provide Ma with the makings of an old-fashioned fish-fry on Saturday night; besides the boys, some of the neighbors would drop in for the feast. Afterward they all sat on the porch steps and, led by Ma's lustrous voice, sang their favorite spirituals in the summer night.

On Sunday afternoons the little gang went for long walks out by the mill, or occasionally they hiked all the way to the fair grounds for the band concert. If they were lucky, they hitched a ride on a farmer's wagon part of the way. One day Paul and Bud promised to meet Charley at the bandstand before the concert. When they arrived he wasn't there yet, and neither was the band, so they climbed the steps and sat on the edge of the platform to wait for him. They saw him coming across the green presently, but he wasn't alone; some strange boy about their age was with him.

"Hi-yi!" Charley yelled as soon as he saw them. "Here's Randolph Tams—his family just moved next door," he introduced the new boy, who had very large ears and a quick smile. Paul and Bud knew right away he would become one of their bunch. Paul had a nickname for him at once—"Randy-Tams." He found out that Randolph would be at Intermediate next year, and they were just getting acquainted when a loud trumpeting from behind the bandstand announced that the players had arrived, so the boys climbed down from the platform and sat in the front row of the bleachers to wait for the concert.

Although they had to work every day during the week, they usually managed to have plenty of fun when Saturday and Sunday came. And of course there was the annual church picnic in July, which all the West Side boys attended somehow, whether they went to church or not. This year the Eaker Street congregation, which was Methodist, combined with two Baptist churches in a joint effort to make the outing better than ever. Paul had talked to Reverend Butler several times after the Easter program, and had decided to choose Eaker Street as his church. He

had joined in May; Bud and Charley followed suit a few
weeks later; and the three of them, with Randy-Tams (who
now made the little group a foursome), stuck together at
the picnic, which was so big it overran the whole fair
grounds. The boys piled their plates high, along with
everybody else, at the long line of tables laden with scrumptious things; then the four of them found a good place to
eat, under some buckeye trees. At the ball game between
the Baptists and the Methodists, held in the afternoon, all
four rooted and cheered for Eaker Street. And they went
home feeling triumphant because their team won in the
ninth inning.

But church picnics were gone in a Sunday, and Monday
morning found the four boys making the rounds again.
Sometimes they paired off—Paul and Bud taking one street,
and Charley and Randolph another—asking at every door,
"Mow your lawn, Ma'm?" "Clip the hedges and rake
leaves?" They had a few regular customers like Captain
Stivers, but most of the people in Dayton took care of their
yards themselves.

Of course there was always Ma's laundry to deliver, but
that did not bring in much extra for Paul. One evening,
when he was coming home with the empty wagon, he
walked along the river, trying to figure a sure way to earn
the school money. He often went down by the river when
he wanted to think—or to dream. It was very still at dusk
now, and so quiet he could hear the killdeer piping across
the water, and the frogs in the marshy edge, with their
deep croaking. In the peaceful atmosphere he forgot his
figuring; before long he had taken out the little notebook
he always carried with him, and began to scribble. When
the sun was gone he went home, feeling rich with a poem
in his pocket.

Early in August Rob came on a short visit; he walked in

unexpectedly one day when Paul was reading aloud to Ma while she ironed. (He had picked up a dime novel someone had left in the lobby of the Beckel Hotel; he enjoyed reading everything that came to hand, from *Deadeye Dick* to *David Copperfield*, though he well knew the difference between the two.) Ma sent him to fetch Will and Meta for supper, and the five of them had a "family reunion" in the kitchen, catching up on the latest news from Cincinnati. Rob had a girl now—"a real girl," he told them—whom he was going to marry as soon as he could afford the ring. He talked so much about Electra Garrison that Paul revived the verses he had scribbled the year before when Will and Meta were engaged. They both got a hearty laugh out of the lines, but Rob didn't find the poem so funny this time.

Before he left the next morning, however, he took Paul aside and slipped a silver dollar into his hand. "Book money," he said shyly. "Part of it, anyway."

"Hey," Paul stared at the shiny big coin. "What about the ring?"

"Nem'mind," Rob smiled. "I'll manage."

"Thanks, Rob." Paul put the money in a special jar he had labeled "School funds," which Ma kept beside the porcelain pig on the shelf. "I'll give it back after graduation."

"Hush yo' mouf, Boy!" Rob said in plantation talk, and they were both chuckling when Ma came in from the backyard.

A penny here, a penny there, a nickel now, a dime later on—it all added up by the end of summer to make enough, with Rob's dollar, for books, paper, pencils, and even a new pair of jeans, so Paul could enter high school in style.

The red brick building, which took up a whole block on Maple Street, rose grandly before his eyes as he came

around the corner on Perry Street the day classes began.
Oh, he had seen Central High many times before, when
he passed by delivering laundry; but it was one thing to
notice a place on the way to some place else, and quite
another to be going inside a huge structure like this, knowing that you were to be part of the life that went on behind
those big walnut doors. He recognized Orville Wright
starting up the steps with some of the other boys he had
known at Intermediate, and he hurried to join them.

"There's Deacon Dunbar," one of them called out, seeing
him. "Hey, Deac! Come on, we'll wait for you."

He ran up the steps and they all went in together.

High school was very much like Intermediate, only
there was a great deal more "doing" all the time, not to
mention a lot more homework for classes. Paul liked his
new teachers, especially Mr. Watkins, the English in-
structor; and he was sure Captain Stivers, who welcomed
them at the opening Assembly, must be the finest principal
in the country.

Ezra Kuhns was in several of Paul's classes, and so was
Orville. Paul and Ezra both signed up for debating, but
Orville was more interested in science than anything else,
though he liked composition, too. He couldn't make words
sing, the way Paul did, but he had a clear, concise style in
setting down scientific facts which made his essays easy to
read. Mr. Watkins was soon reading aloud the compositions both boys wrote for English.

High school would have been a breeze for Paul if it
hadn't been for the old bugbear of mathematics. So far as
he was concerned, algebra was nothing but a more horrify-
ing form of arithmetic, designed to frighten backward
students into studying. And his algebra teacher didn't help
any when it came to explaining the subject. She was a
wizened little German woman, with a face like a dried-up

apple. She expected the pupils to catch on to the thus and therefore of "*a* plus *b*"—or "*x* minus *y*"—and to terms like "equation, summation, negation" with practically no explanation. She showed them how to do a problem once, on the blackboard; if someone didn't understand and raised his hand to ask questions, as Paul did during the first week, she gave him a furious look, brought her fist down on the desk, and shouted, "Dummkopf! How many times do I haf to tell you?" Then she would go over the problem in a sarcastic voice, pounding the desk all through to emphasize her words. After their first surprise, the boys and girls began to giggle at "Dummkopf" and continued quivering hysterically, some openly guffawing, until the whole thing ended like a burlesque, with the teacher only making it funnier by keeping right on with her tirade in spite of the commotion.

Paul's low laughter was as contagious as anybody's; but he and the others, who were innocent enough to expect more information from the teacher, soon stopped asking questions.

"She won't give you a straight answer, no matter what you want to know," he complained to Orville as they were walking home from school toward the end of September. He had just been describing the scene, giving a perfect imitation of the teacher for Orville, who was in stitches.

"What don't you understand about algebra, Paul?" he asked when he stopped chortling. The subject was all perfectly clear to him.

"Only four things," Paul said.

Orville cocked an eyebrow at him. "That all?"

"Sure. Equation, summation, negation and variation!" He ran them all together the way the teacher had.

Orville laughed then, but after a minute he offered, "Tell you what: I'll help you with algebra, if you'll help me with

the poem we have to write for English next week; I'm all
right at essays, but when it comes to poetry I'm a dud."
He shook his head.

"The deal's on!" Paul agreed, and they shook hands.

Orville suddenly stopped short and stared around him.
"Look where I've come!"

Paul was as surprised as Orville to find they were in
front of the railroad tracks near his house. The two boys
had discovered soon after school opened that they went
home in the same direction for a good part of the way.
They cut across Maple Street to Perry, and walked down
Perry as far as Fifth together. After that, while Paul went
south on the other side of the railroad tracks, Orville
crossed the bridge, going west to the Wright home at No.
7 Hawthorne Street. But today he had been so interested
in Paul's story that he completely forgot to turn onto the
bridge, nor did Paul realize they had passed it till Orville
stopped.

It would not be the only time one or the other of the
boys went eight or ten blocks out of the way before they
knew it. They were always so busy talking that they lost
sight of time, place and distance.

They stayed late in study hall for several afternoons so
Orville could show Paul how "simple" it was to work out
a formula in algebra, and Paul could repay him by pointing
out how "easy" it was to put ideas in rhyme and meter.
Neither one was ever convinced that the other's subject
was such a cinch, but they both received passing marks—
Paul barely made it in algebra—so they were satisfied.

But if Paul did not shine in mathematics, he was a star in
other fields. He and Ezra outdid each other in debate and
Paul was soon known all over school for his wit and sharp
retort. In English class Mr. Watkins suggested that some
of his poems were good enough to be printed, and Paul

went sailing home to copy a few and send them in to the *Dayton Herald*, which devoted a regular column to poetry on the back page. Occasionally they published the work of an unknown, if they thought it could stand up beside Tennyson or Browning or any of the established poets whose lines usually filled the column. The paper didn't offer any money for the use of poems, but Paul hardly gave a thought to payment; the joy of seeing his work in print would be reward enough. He told Ma to save the editions of the *Herald* that usually came wrapped around the laundry bundles, and each night he smoothed out the back page to see if his lines were in the poetry column. He didn't tell Ma what he was looking for; he wanted to surprise her if the time ever came—months went by and there was no sign that the *Herald* had even received the work of one Paul Laurence Dunbar.

But he didn't give up. He kept on sending the paper every poem that drew special praise from Mr. Watkins; and in the meantime he did break into print at school. The Central High *Times* carried a "contribution" from him nearly every month. He felt almost as proud as if it had been the *Herald* when he showed the first one to Ma.

"Mr. Watkins says they hardly ever print a freshman's work," he told her, trying to keep down the excitement in his voice.

Ma folded the little newspaper carefully and placed it on the table in the parlor, right beside the red plush runner. "So's the company can see it," she said.

Every time he brought home a copy containing one of his poems or compositions, she put it on top, and before long there was a little pile of them on the parlor table. Ma was beginning to see that Paul was cut out to be a writer; she had wanted him to become a preacher after he had done so well on the Easter program, but Paul had other ideas. He had visions of books, packed with poems; or short stories; or a long novel—all of them bearing his name in big letters.

But Ma had pointed out that being a preacher was such a respectable calling. It was one of the few professions in which a Negro could rise to the top. He would always wear a white collar and a cutaway coat, and people would listen to his words.

"They'll listen," Paul had said, and then he had been quiet. It was the closest he and Ma had ever come to an argument, and he didn't want to quarrel with her. At thirteen he knew what he wanted to do, just as Charley wanted to be a preacher, and Bud had decided to become a doctor, if he could find a way to go through college.

Ma realized, as the pile of papers grew, and Paul's marks in "Literature" were close to 100, that poetry rushed out of his soul like a fountain; and she would be the last one to turn off the stream of beauty.

When summer came she decided to move into a larger house so she could rent out a room; that way Paul would be sure of staying in school another year anyhow. Boarders paid well, her neighbors told her—and what if it meant a little extra labor, a worse backache at night? Paul's education was worth everything. And one day in October, when he came home with a special light in his eyes, Ma knew she was right even before he spoke.

"Guess what, Ma," he said, waltzing her around the kitchen. But he couldn't wait—he had to tell her right off. "The boys at school elected me to Philomathean!"

Ma knew how much the honor meant to Paul. She had heard him talk about the debating and literary society all during his freshman year. It was the most important club at Central.

"I'm happy for you, Son," she said. She couldn't begin

to tell him how happy the membership made her, what it meant to her, an ex-slave, to have her boy accepted on equal terms with the sons of white men. She smiled instead, a twinkle in her dark eyes. "Only thing s'prises me is they didn't elect you long ago!"

Paul laughed, too, but he knew that Ma was covering up her feelings. They came out in song at her work that night—"All God's Chillun Got Wings," "Golden Slippers," and always, "Swing Low, Sweet Chariot." And as she sang, she resolved once more that Paul would finish high school. There was still a mountain of prejudice in the world, she knew, but if anything could tear down the barrier between peoples it was education. Since Emancipation, schools were the common meeting ground for the young of all races and religions, and the children who worked out the questions of learning together would grow up to work out the problems of life together.

Paul's gang was almost as pleased as he with his election to Philo. They were all at Central this year—Bud, Charley, and Randy—so the foursome were together in school and out of it, although they were in different classes. Bud Burns was living at Captain Stivers now, acting as yardman in exchange for his board and schooling; he had enrolled in a full premedical course, and the Principal was doing all he could to help a boy with such ambition.

On Saturday mornings the bunch often gathered at the Captain's, and while Bud clipped the hedges they all stood around talking together, or they would take turns with the clippers—the Captain didn't mind, so long as the job was done. Sometimes Paul would go up to the little workshop on the top floor of the house, where Captain Stivers spent many hours at his hobby, violin-making. Paul loved to watch him shape the scroll and cut the fine wood, add the finger boards, strings, and pegs, and finally the tail piece.

It was painstaking work, but to the Captain it was a labor of love; and once, when he was polishing an instrument he had just completed, he told Paul the story of the violin-maker of Cremona, the great Stradivari, whose violins, like those of his master, Amati, were works of art as well as instruments which produced tones of the purest beauty.

Wide eyed, Paul laid a reverent finger on the edge of the violin. "More beautiful than this?"

The Captain laughed. "Thanks, Paul—but this is far from being a Stradivarius, believe me . . . except to me," he added softly.

"And to me," Paul said to himself. These were the first violins he had seen at such close range, and to him a Stivers was as graceful as a Stradivarius. He loved the music they sent streaming out of their strings, and he hoped he could play the fiddle himself some day—not professionally, but for the fun of it, joyously; like the fiddler who poured out tunes for the West Side socials, till they all got "itching heels." Or sometimes he might play a haunting melody that whispered of times gone by.

"Hal-loo-oo, Paul!" He heard his name called from below. The boys had finished, and were ready to start off for the Dayton View bridge with their poles and pails of worms.

"Excuse me, Captain Stivers, I have to go," he said. "Thank you for letting me watch."

"Glad to have you any time, Paul," the Captain said.

The fish were not biting, though it was a warm October day, the beginning of Indian summer. The others held their poles diligently, lifting them every now and then to make sure the bait was still on the hook, or to put on a fresh worm in the hope of making a catch. But Paul wanted to enjoy the day. He took off his shoes and socks

and waded along the edge of the bank till he found a sandy
spot under a weeping willow. He pulled some string out
of his pocket, and tied the fishing pole to his big toe. Then
he stretched out on the sand, and gazed at the brilliant
October sky through the long green tresses of the willow
tree. Far away, the gentle Ohio hills were ablaze with red
and gold autumn leaves, and purple ironweed glowed in the
meadow. The air smelt of apples and woodsmoke. He
idled away half an hour or so in dreams, but after a while
he had to write something down on paper. He took out his
notebook, and rolled on his side, keeping his fishing toe up
in the air. He wet the tip of the pencil thoughtfully, and
set down a stanza; an hour or more passed as he wrote,
crossed out and rewrote:

> October is the treasurer of the year,
>   And all the months pay bounty to her store;
> The fields and orchards still their tribute bear,
>   And fill her brimming coffers more and more.
> But she, with youthful lavishness,
> Spends all her wealth in gaudy dress,
>   And decks herself in garments bold
>   Of scarlet, purple, red, and gold.

He hesitated, wondering how to begin the next stanza.
He wanted to say that October was a spendthrift of time—
but how? He nibbled the eraser-end of the pencil, trying
to find the right phrase, when all of a sudden something (a
"big one" from the way it felt) nibbled at his bait, tugging
so hard it pulled over line, pole, and Paul, who rolled on
his stomach, right on top of the notebook! He grabbed it,
putting it back in his pocket as he sat up and gave the pole
a quick jerk to set the hook; then he took a second to
untie his toe with one hand while he steadied the pole with
the other—the fish was a fighter. As soon as he was free,

he stood up and dug his feet in the sand to brace himself. His fish put up a battle, but he hung on, though the bamboo swayed and bent over the water in the struggle.

A short way off, Randy, Bud and Charley, who had seen Paul rise up from the bank like a rocket, came toward him quietly, waiting to see what kind of a catch he had. The fight went on a few minutes more, and then, with one mighty heave, Paul pulled up an enormous river carp, with a great big rubbery mouth.

"Yippee!" The boys ran down the bank, cheering.

"What you got there, Boy?"

"Mmm . . . mmp! That's somepin!" Randy waggled his ears and rolled his eyes in admiration when Paul held the scaly fish high so everyone could see.

"How come none of us nabbed a whopper like that?" Charley wondered. "All we caught was a dinky perch."

Bud chuckled softly. "I guess Paul has the best system. You lie and doze, and pretty soon a big one swims right up and gets himself caught."

Paul laughed with the others. He didn't bother to mention the fact that he had been far from dozing when the carp struck.

That night, after they had devoured the fish, which Ma fried a crispy golden brown, the boys sat around feeling contented, lazily trying to decide what to do.

"I know!" Randy snapped his fingers suddenly. "The minstrel show down at the Lodge!"

"How did we forget?" Paul said. "I'm sure we can usher."

"Let's go." Charley jumped up, ready to start.

So they all slicked back their hair, straightened their ties, and set off for the Knights of Pythias Hall on Fifth Street, where the West Side Lodge, No. 5, held its meetings and entertainments. None of the boys had ever seen a minstrel show; this was, in fact, the first to be presented in Dayton, although the "blackface" comedians were becoming more and more popular all over the country. Ever since the days of Dan Rice, and George Christy (who made a tremendous hit with his show in New York in 1860), actors had been smudging their faces with burnt cork, adding a wide band of white around their mouths to make themselves into exaggerated portraits of so-called "darkies,"—plantation types that were no more true than the stage Scotchman, with his stinginess and exaggerated burr.

But minstrel shows had caught on, until colored actors themselves blacked their faces, sang the minstrels, and cracked jokes in a twisted language that was not really Negro dialect, nor plantation talk as Paul knew it from Ma and her friends, but a crazy distortion of words. The minstrel-show Negro was nothing but a buffoon, a scamp-tramp-clown figure who could never arouse anything but raucous laughter unmixed with feelings of sympathy or understanding.

Nevertheless, Paul and his gang were as curious as the rest of the people to see exactly what a minstrel show was like, and they found the hall overflowing when they reached the Lodge.

The president of the Lodge was glad to put the boys on as extra ushers, handing out programs, directing people to the right row, and anything else to help seat the audience before the show went on. They had not expected such a large crowd. But when the curtains parted, to the tune of "Look Away, Dixieland," struck up by the little West Side band, everybody was in place, even the boys, with their eyes glued to the stage.

Five actors were on the platform, all dressed alike in black and white, wearing derby hats, and of course with their faces an inky black save for the chalk-white ring around their mouths. The man in the middle was "Mr. Interlocutor," who asked questions of the two "end men" on each side of him.

After a few "jokes" in heavy dialect, and in twisted words (like "dictionamary"), the first and last men took up their banjos and began to strum. Then all five sang a chorus of some song, but would break it off abruptly for more jokes. That was all there was to a minstrel show.

The audience appeared to enjoy it, but Paul thought it must be because the people had so little entertainment of any sort. The boys talked about the performance all the way home.

"If you ask me, we could put on a better show than that," Paul said. He stopped suddenly in the middle of the road as they were crossing Fifth Street. "Hey! Why don't we try it?"

"Jes what yo' mean, Mr. Interlocutah?" Randy asked slyly. "A ministrel show?"

Paul laughed with the others, but he shook his head as he continued across the road. "No, I mean a regular play, like those at the Bijou."

"How can the four of us put on plays?" Bud asked.

"We'd get some of the others," Paul said. "Ennis, Jake Payne, . . . we could start a West Side boys dramatic club at Central," he finished.

"Sounds good to me," Bud said, and the other two agreed.

"Only we ought to have a literary name," Paul went on.

"Like what?" Charley asked.

"Well, like Philomathean." Paul mentioned the one which naturally came to his mind first; for a new member, he was already very active in the debating society. "That means 'love of learning'." He paused a moment, thinking.

Then he grinned. "I've got it! How about Philodramian—love of drama?"

Philodramian it was, and the boys lost no time in organizing their club. Monday after school they rounded up four more neighborhood boys—Jake, Ennis, Charley Mathews and Will Shaw. No girls, they decided. Girls were always giggling when you wanted to get something done. Oh, there were a few who could help with costumes and props; Paul's cousin, Dora Burton and her bunch—Eugenie Griffin, Della Butler, Katie Wilson, the Finley sisters, and one or two others, like Lily Hill, whom Paul was taking to a Halloween party at the church.

The club met twice a month at Ma's house. There they could rehearse to their hearts' content, no younger brothers or sisters to bother them, nor older ones to criticize. It provided good entertainment for Ma, who enjoyed hearing the boys rehearse their speeches while she ironed. And since she knew that boys are always hungry, she usually had a pan of hot gingerbread ready for them after a meeting.

Paul wrote the first play to be presented. It was called "The Stolen Calf," and was all about a bunch of boys who steal a farmer's calf so they can buy tickets for the circus.

"Ministers won't like that," Charley Higgins objected when Paul told the boys the plot. Since they planned to perform their play in churches, they had to be careful, he said.

"Wait a minute, Preacher," Paul smiled. "When the school Principal finds out what the boys have done, he makes them give back the calf, and buys them tickets to the circus himself. Then he puts the boys to work in his yard to earn the money for the tickets. What do you say now?"

"Fine," Charley agreed.

"The Stolen Calf" was given first at the Baptist church, in Yellow Springs, and was so successful it was put on at other churches in and around Dayton. The boys charged a slight admission, half of which went into the poor-box, and half into their treasury ("our own poor-box," Paul said). The little troupe soon built up a reputation around town, and when entertainment was needed, Philodramian was called on for a performance. One of the Lodge members gave Paul a pair of old dueling swords, and he immediately wrote a play to match them. Ma's kitchen resounded with the clash of sabers for quite a while, and the girls had a terrible time with the costumes, which were supposed to be medieval; but the production was finally completed, and as successful as the first one. Paul was very proud of the swords, which he hung, crossed, on the wall above his bed; and he kept them for many years after Philodramian days were over.

At Central everybody knew about the club, and Paul was one of the most popular boys in his class. As he went down the hall to his locker each morning, he had to stop every little way when some boy called, "Say, Deac, I want to see you"; or, "Hey, Deac, how about writing a poem for the paper next week?" Or some girl would stop him with, "Paul, can you come to my party next Friday night?" (Of course he always accepted the invitations.)

The high school *Times* was always asking for contributions, and about the middle of the year, he was appointed "Assistant Editor." There was the title—he showed it to Ma with a beaming smile—and right beside it was his name: "Paul Laurence Dunbar, '90." He himself put that issue at the top of the pile on the parlor table.

Orville could have had a post on the *Times*, but he was all wrapped up in a newspaper of his own. He and Wilbur had just started a two-page weekly called *The Midget*, which was already gaining circulation in the West Side, since it carried mostly neighborhood news, and people liked to read about themselves. The Wright brothers had rigged up a homemade printing press in their father's barn, where they did everything from writing news items, obituaries, and ad copy to setting type and printing. Paul found the Wrights' barn a fascinating place on Saturday morning when the paper went to press, and he usually got there early to watch.

"Hi, Deac!" Orville called one morning in February as Paul's head appeared at the top of the stairs leading to the loft that served as their workshop. "How are you?"

"Fine," Paul said, coughing a little. He still came down with colds in the winter and had been absent from school a couple of days.

"Your cold all gone?" Orville asked.

"Oh, sure." Paul unwound the old red wool muffler Ma had made him wear around his neck. "That little ol' cough don't mean a thing. I'm in the best of health."

Orville was busy setting a line of type. "Thanks, Deac," he said when he finished.

"Huh? What for?"

Orville beckoned him over and pointed to the letters he had just put in place. "I needed a 'filler'," he said.

Paul read, "Deacon Dunbar is in good health." He grinned. "That should keep 'em guessing!"

"I thought so." Orville grinned back at him.

Orville showed Paul the mysteries of "putting the paper to bed"—typesetting, locking the forms, inking the press, and running off the copies. Since he was mechanically minded, he handled that end of the business, while Wilbur took care of the advertising and wrote copy. In a very short time, *The Midget* grew to the point where the boys felt it deserved a more dignified name so the paper was rechristened, *The West Side News*. Ed Sines, another Central High student, joined the staff as "business manager," which really meant advertising salesman; he brought in so much business that the boys abandoned the barn and moved to a small shop on West Third Street. Orville built a new printing press himself; nobody but he knew exactly how it worked; in fact, one of the printers from the Dayton *Herald* who saw the contraption said it was a miracle that the paper got printed at all. But it did, and only Orville knew the secret.

Paul was usually on hand at the shop Saturday mornings as he had been at the barn. Ezra came there regularly, too, and the jokes and quips flew out as fast as the copies of the latest edition came flipping out of Orville's press.

In the midst of all these goings-on, Ma had a letter from Rob, who had married Electra Garrison and moved to Chicago. Now he was urging the whole family to come to the big city—Will and Meta, Ma and Paul. Money was freer, jobs were easier to get, and Chicago offered all kinds of opportunities that Dayton did not.

"What do you say, Paul?" Ma asked when she finished reading the letter. "Will and Meta are thinking of going; maybe we should, too." She was not at all sure what they should do.

Paul, however, had no doubts in his mind. Leave Dayton? Leave Central High, which had the best principal in the world in Captain Stivers and good English teachers like Mr. Watkins and Mrs. Truesdale? Leave all his friends in Philomathean, and his own Philodramian? Leave the fun at the Wright brothers' printing office? And the peaceful sight of the Miami River flowing close by? And the low, tree-covered hills, so beautiful in spring and fall? Leave all he loved for a strange, noisy big city? No, thanks!

"Let Will and Meta go if they like," he said. "I don't want to move, Ma. Do you?"

"Not if you don't, Paul," Ma said. "And anyway, what would an old washerwoman like me do in Chicago?"

Paul smiled at her. "Don't you worry, Ma. When I get out of school I'll take care of you," he promised.

Late in the term, when he had almost forgotten to look for them, two of Paul's poems appeared in the Dayton *Herald*. He discovered the first on the eighth of June, just as he was about to throw away the paper wrapped around one of the laundry bundles. He had stopped watching the poetry column because he didn't want to be disappointed any more. But that day something made him glance at the back page, and there it was: " 'Our Martyred Soldiers,' by Paul Laurence Dunbar."

"Ma!" He waved the crumpled page in front of her eyes. "Oh, Ma, look!" They read it together. The poem was not very different from any nineteenth century verse extolling heroes, but it was good, as such poetry goes, and the *Herald* had thought well enough of it to publish it—the important fact for Paul just then.

The second one appeared only five days later, on June 13, 1888. It was the poem he had written beside the Miami on that quiet evening last summer, and it was a much better piece of work than the first. This one had the flavor of originality, the stamp of true poetry. He had called it simply, "On The River." It began:

> The sun is low,
> The waters flow,
> My boat is dancing to and fro.
> The eve is still,
> Yet from the hill
> The killdeer echoes loud and shrill.

The other three stanzas kept the same meter, the same mood. None of the poems suggested by Professor Wilson as models had followed a pattern or rhyme scheme like this. Here was no copyist of old poets; here was a new poet, Paul Laurence Dunbar, a boy of sixteen, and he was only beginning to express himself.

CHAPTER VIII

Picnic

HE WENT to school early the next morning, his heart humming with happiness, his brain buzzing with a dozen different ideas for new poems. Half-way across the vacant lot, he stooped to pluck a field daisy, stuck it in his coat lapel, and continued jauntily up over the railroad tracks. It was one of those "rare" June days that James Russell Lowell had described in "The Vision of Sir Launfal," which they had studied in Literature class the week before. Heaven certainly had laid her "warm ear" over the earth today, Paul thought as he gazed up at the clear blue sky, where wisps of "mare's tails" were drifting lazily by. For a moment he was tempted to turn off the road and head toward the river, where he could wander alone along the water's edge during this hour or so before school. But he had promised to meet the president of Philo-

mathean and one or two others in study hall; they were
going to draw up a list from which the members would
choose the subject for the final debate of the year at the
regular meeting after school. He didn't want to give the
boys any chance to regret that they had elected him to
the club, so he continued straight on to Maple Street.

The halls were empty at this hour, but on the way to
his locker he heard someone behind him call, "Hello, Paul,"
and he turned around. It was Lily Hill, who had come
in a moment after he did.

"Wait for me!" She hurried her steps, and the click-
clack of her high-buttoned shoes with their sharp heels
echoed daintily down the hall.

"Well, Lily, what're you doing at school so early?" Paul
teased her as she came up. "Getting studious all of a sudden?"

"Now, Paul," she pouted, shaking a finger at him. "Just
because you're smarter than the rest of us . . ." She broke
off, looking at him reproachfully. She was straight and
slim as a pear tree, and she was wearing a white ribbon in
her hair. "I came early because I have a theme to write,
and when I saw you I . . . thought you might help me with
it."

Paul shook his head. "I have to go to a Philomathean
committee meeting, Lily."

Her face brightened. "What's it about?"

"Subjects for the last debate of the year."

"Oh." She seemed disappointed. She lingered hopefully for a minute or two, as if she expected him to say
something else, but when he did not, she went back toward
her locker, waving her hanky at him. "Good-by, Paul."

"Good-by, Lily." As he continued down the hall, Paul
could easily guess why Lily had been lingering. She was
probably expecting him to ask her to the Philo picnic which

was to take place just before graduation. She had invited him to several parties and it was time for him to "return the favor" as they said. But he was not at all sure he wanted to take Lily to the picnic. She was pretty, but she wasn't nearly as nice nor as much fun as some of the other girls. He would have to decide which one to invite pretty soon. Right now he hurried toward the study hall, hoping Lily hadn't made him late.

The boys were already there; he could hear them talking earnestly about something when he was still outside the room. But when he opened the door, they suddenly stopped, staring at him, and then at each other in embarrassed silence. It was only for a second, but Paul could feel the friction in the air as sharply as if he'd had an electric shock. Robert LaRue, the president, recovered first.

"Here's the Deacon now—I guess we can start!" He said heartily—a little too heartily.

"Hi, Deac!" and "How's our champion point-getter?" the other two followed him up quickly.

Paul sensed that he must have been the subject of their conversation when he came in, but he couldn't imagine why. If he had done anything wrong, they wouldn't be so overly cordial. However, he wasn't going to let on that he realized they were acting queerly.

"Sorry I'm late," he said. "Girl trouble." He winked.

The boys laughed a little, but it was strained, he felt, and he could have sworn that LaRue's face grew red. Maybe the whole thing was his imagination, but he didn't think so. He waited another moment while the uncomfortable silence continued, and then he suggested, "Should we get started? I have a list here." He fished around in his pocket and drew out a folded paper. "Just a couple of ideas that came to me while I was eating breakfast."

The boys got down to business at once, and the air cleared. By the time other students started coming in for study, and the bells rang for class, the four of them, led by Paul, had completed a sizable list of subjects and picked out one that they preferred above the rest, which they would push for at the meeting. There had been no further evidence of strain or embarrassment; as the group left the study hall, LaRue even congratulated Paul on having his poems published in the *Herald*. "I feel as if we had a real celebrity in the club," he said.

"Thanks, Rob." Paul's face lit up. "I just saw the first one by accident myself." He told them how he had almost thrown the paper away. The other two said they had missed it, but they were going to look up last Friday's edition of the *Herald* in the library right away. The four separated, and Paul went whistling down the hall. He was sure now that he had been mistaken.

He had a full day, working on copy in the *Times* office at lunch hour while he munched the sandwiches Ma had packed for him; seeing people between classes about *Tomfoolery*, a tiny, hand-lettered monthly he and a few others put together for pure fun. *Tomfoolery* was full of jokes, quips, puns, and jingles by the dozen, many of the last written by Paul during dull periods in mathematics class. Today Ernest Blumenschtein, who belonged to Philomathean and had a flair for cartooning, showed him a drawing he had made at the last Philo meeting. There were all the members—LaRue behind the desk, Tom Whyte, Ernest (who was not as good at debating as he was in art work), and Paul himself in the front row. Ezra, standing up in the back, was waving his hand wildly, his glasses falling down on his nose.

Paul chuckled. "This is one of the best you've done, Ernie," he said. "Will it take ink?"

"Sure thing," Ernest said. He was pleased.

"Then we'll use it in *Tomfoolery*. Bring it around Friday when we 'go to press'." They both laughed at the phrase. They made only one copy of the little fun-sheet, and charged five cents a look. Most of the students found it well worth the nickel; the paper was frayed and worn by the time it had passed through the hands of all who wanted to see it.

With one thing and another, Paul was again a few minutes late when he got to the Philo meeting room after school. From the sound of the voices he heard there must be quite a number inside already. But again he was greeted by a sudden silence as soon as he opened the door; it was so strange! He felt queer all over, but his tone was light-hearted.

"What's the matter—am I being black-balled for being late?" he asked, pretending to be worried.

The boys giggled nervously, but at the same time they seemed relieved. He wasn't late, they assured him; LaRue wasn't there yet, neither was Dohn. Ernest showed him the drawing, which he had already inked up, and somebody else consulted him about writing a poem for a special occasion. A minute later, the president came in, followed by Dohn, and the meeting started. After much heated discussion, not to say argument, the young debaters voted on the list of subjects, and chose the one the boys had picked out in the morning. The meeting adjourned.

Paul walked out with Ezra, who asked him casually, "Are you taking Lily Hill to the picnic, Deac?"

It was an odd question for Ezra to ask, Paul thought. He hadn't decided yet, he told Ezra, and added, "Why, Ez?"

His friend shrugged his shoulders, squinting at him

through his gold-rimmed glasses. "No reason; I just wondered."

"Don't you like Lily?"

"Oh, sure; she's all right," Ezra said quickly.

"Then what . . ." Paul began but he stopped in the
middle. It suddenly dawned on him that this must have
been what the boys were conferring about both times they
stopped talking when he came up. He had an idea what
was worrying them. The boys wouldn't have thought
twice about his attending the picnic, with or without a girl;
but he knew they were afraid their girls might object.
(Central High girls were more backward about such things
than the boys.) He also knew that although the boys might
hash it over from morning till night, none of them could
bring themselves to say anything to him. Good old Ezra
was trying to let him know, without hurting his feelings.
Paul decided to make it easy for him.

"I don't even know if I'll go to the picnic," he said.
"I'm so far behind in math, I'll have to spend my spare time
boning up or I'll fail."

If Ezra thought he was only acting, he didn't say so.
And in the next few days, Paul dropped remarks here and
there, cheerfully, so the boys wouldn't be embarrassed.
"Sorry, I won't be able to get to the picnic . . . too much
work to do." "Sounds like a swell picnic . . . too bad I
won't be able to make it."

In the meantime, an idea had been growing in his mind,
and when the dramatic club met at Ma's on Thursday
night, he proposed that Philodramian hold a picnic to
celebrate its success. The boys hailed the plan; they had
plenty of money in the treasury since the last performance.

"Let's have the best doggone picnic Central High ever
saw," Randy said.

"Let's do something different," Bud added. "What do you say, Paul?"

"Sure," Paul agreed. He thought a minute. What could they plan that would be unusual—that no one else at school had done? He snapped his fingers. "I've got it! How about hiring a canal boat for the day, and holding our picnic down by the Narrows?"

"Hoo-ray!" The boys cheered.

They appointed Paul and Bud to see about chartering the boat, so the two went down to the Canal Street offices, and found it cost five dollars a day, which included the fee for the captain.

He informed Paul and Bud that the trip would start at ten o'clock in the morning, and they would get to the Narrows Landing around one thirty. The club would have several hours for the picnic, and the return trip would be made at twilight, starting at six o'clock sharp. The schedule sounded fine to the boys; the captain warned them he wouldn't wait for any blanketty-blank stragglers either way, but they assured him everybody would be on time. They hired the boat for the following Saturday.

Plans went on all week long. The boys consulted Ma about the menu; they asked her and several other mothers to be chaperones and cooks; and they paid for the food out of the club treasury. They invited all the girls who had worked on costumes and sets, including Lily Hill, who was happy as a lark over the invitation. As the week went on, preparations increased. On Friday delicious baking smells came wafting out of Ma's oven from morning till night; apple pies and cookies, and a big cake were in the making, but all the boys got was the tantalizing odor; she shooed them away when they came near the kitchen.

On Saturday everybody was to meet at the dock at a quarter to ten. Bud came over early to find Ma and Paul

waiting with bulging baskets. He and Paul took hold of
the handles, and they set off in high spirits. The sun was
already beaming down on what would probably be the
hottest day in June as they boarded the Third Street horse
car bound for Canal Street. In summer the cars were open
all the way, and you could hop on anywhere and slide into
a seat right there if it was empty. Today quite a number
of people were on the car when the four horses came to a
halt at the corner; Paul and Bud had to go past the middle
before they climbed in and held a place for Ma on one of
the cane-back benches. The driver slapped the reins on
the horses' rumps, starting them up again, and the conductor came along to collect the five-cent fare. Everybody seemed to be in a holiday mood, laughing, gossiping,
and enjoying the breeze that blew in on all sides once they
were moving.

When the horse car pulled up at the Canal Street dock,
Paul and Bud, ready to jump off, stopped in their tracks
and stared at each other. Instead of a cluster of girls and
some of the other members, a whole crowd stood there
waiting!

"Where did they all come from?" Paul wondered out
loud; and in the next breath, "What'll we do, Ma?"

"Don't worry, there's plenty for all," Ma said, hopping
off the car. "And anyhow, 'pears to me a good many of
'em have baskets."

So they did. The three arrivals were hailed as they came
up, and introduced to sisters, brothers, cousins and neighbors of the girls and other members; everybody who had
heard about the picnic decided to come along—and who
could turn them down, on a beautiful sunshiny day in
June, with the canal boat just waiting to carry them off on a
brand new spree? The more the merrier!

As soon as the last latecomers appeared, the crowd moved

on board, spreading out over the broad, flat deck. The Captain gave the signal to the canaler onshore, who cracked his whip over the three-span mule team which pulled the boat, walking single file along the narrow towpath. A gleeful shout went up from the crowd—they were off!

To be sure, it was a slow passage through the sluggish waters, but they had plenty of time. In twos and threes the girls and boys roamed about the deck, investigating everything. The captain's wife showed them the living quarters, and the pens on the afterdeck where an extra mule team used to be stabled for long hauls. The Captain himself, his mustaches bristling in the breeze, was surrounded by a changing group from time to time, as he steered the boat, or called out orders to the teamster on the towpath— orders usually rounded off by a hearty oath, but few could hear it above the shouts and laughter of the carefree passengers. Paul sat on deck with Lily, Eugenie Griffin and Bud, watching the willow trees and low shrubs that bordered the canal pass slowly in front of his eyes as the boat glided by.

They reached the Narrows Landing at exactly one thirty for all their meandering. Everybody piled off the boat and made for the picnic grounds in a grove of shady elms. The boys put a number of tables together, and Ma, with the other chaperones and some of the girls, began opening baskets and setting out the food. The rest wandered through the paths, or watched the Captain tie up and fodder the mules. Three small boys (brothers of the Finley girls) ran around all over, climbing the low trees and swinging from the branches like wicked monkeys. Before long, Ma called them all to come and have some "eats."

What a spread it was! No church picnic ever boasted a more loaded board. Sandwiches, hard-boiled eggs, fried chicken; baked beans and yams (still warm in earthenware

pots); homemade pickles and peaches; pies, cookies, and
Ma's special three-layer chocolate cake, with icing an inch
thick . . . mm-mm! At the end of the table stood pitchers
of pink lemonade, which Charley Higgins' mother had
brought in a big jug.

It was all so good everybody went back a second time,
and when Randolph had to try a third helping of his
favorite treat, Paul put it in rhyme:

> Randy-Tams
> Loves candied yams

he sang out, and even Randy himself hooted. But at last
none of them could eat another crumb, and they lolled on
the grass like stuffed sausages. No one could dream of
playing the games they had planned; baseball, relay races,
peanut pushing contests were out of the question. But
presently Paul piped up, "I'm thinking of a word that
begins with the letter 'B.' There was a chorus of, "Oh,
good! Let's play it with three-syllable words!" and a
wail from Lily, "I just know I'll be a 'ghost' right away."

"No, you won't, Lily," said Mabel Finley. She was sitting next to Paul, and added the letter "R"; Bud, beside
her, tacked on an "I." And so it went, around the circle.
If you ended a word, you became one-third of a "ghost";
if you ended two more, you were a whole "ghost" and
were "out" or you could pay a forfeit to the one who
started the word, and stay in. Needless to say, the fine was
always the same, and it was not long before Lily was
planting a kiss on Paul's face.

After a while, they all felt up to the exertion of the races
and contests, but by the time the Captain blew the warning
whistle at a quarter to six, they were ready to gather up
the baskets and other belongings and head for the canal
boat.

On the way home, they watched the sun set over the still waters of the canal. And when the pale moon rose in the west, two or three who had brought their banjos began to strum the tunes of the day, and they sang "By the Light of the Silvery Moon," "Down By the Old Mill Stream," and "My Best Gal." Then someone asked Ma to lead them in a few spirituals, and they all lifted their voices in the clear night air. As the boat neared Canal Street, they softly intoned, "Home, Sweet Home," which ended the singing, and the picnic.

It had been a great success; and Paul remarked to Ma afterward with a chuckle: "I'm so glad the fellows in Philomathean gave me the idea!"

CHAPTER IX

Last Years at "Old Central"

URING HIS senior year Paul began to think of going to college. Some of the boys in Philomathean were talking about it; and Bud, with the goal of medicine straight before him, was already trying to secure a loan so he could go to Harvard. It was ambitious, but the chances of finding men who would back a medical student, or one studying law, were fairly good. Law and medicine were both professions that paid well as a rule, and Negroes were needed in both fields. A boy who became a doctor or lawyer was a "safe risk."

But a writer—who would back a weaver of words, Negro or white, with his chances of financial failure equal to, if not greater, than his success? Paul knew he would have a difficult time getting to college, more so than Bud, and for another reason: he had Ma to consider; she couldn't go on working indefinitely for his education. (Only a few weeks ago, when she had been sent downtown by a housewife to collect a laundry bill, the woman's husband, as he handed her the money, asked: "Why isn't Paul doing this? He's a bad boy!" Ma had come home furious. "I thought something," she told Paul, "but I didn't say it out loud—that old busybody!") Yet, in spite of all the obstacles, Paul had dreams of going to Harvard with Bud, and studying literature in the shadow of Emerson, Longfellow, Whittier and Lowell.

In the meantime, he was busier than ever this year with writing jobs at school. He did more and more of the work on the *Times,* besides turning out poems for special occasions, sometimes as last-minute requests. By now everybody knew his facility with words. He could write a comic poem one day, and a dirge the next, as the occasion demanded. When the senior class boys wanted a ballad about lager beer in German dialect, to be recited at a "stag party," Paul obliged. And when one of their classmates died suddenly during the following week, Paul was called upon to write the memorial ode for the paper.

He was so taken up with all his activities he hardly had time to spend even a part of his Saturday mornings at the Wrights' printing shop, but he did like to keep in touch with the way the little newspaper was faring. And one day around the middle of December, he dropped in at the shop, to find things humming.

Orville was busy at the press, running off a pile of leaflets. Ed and Wilbur were making up a "dummy" of the *West Side News;* they had so many ads they didn't know where to place them all. But more than the paper, the printing business was thriving; the batch of leaflets was only one of a number of jobs the Wright brothers were getting out for various firms in Dayton.

"Sit down, Deac," Orville waved him to a bench near the press, cluttered with extra copies, proof sheets and the like. "We've got a rush order for the Bijou—special performance of *East Lynne*."

Paul pushed aside one of the piles and squeezed onto the bench. The job printing was doing very well, Orville shouted to him over the noise of the press; in two or three months, he figured, they could move to larger quarters, and double their output. He might even build a bigger press.

Ed Sines called over, "He's got great plans for us, hasn't he, Deac?"

Paul nodded, smiling. On a sudden thought, he took a pencil out of his pocket, and wrote on the wall above the press:

> Orville Wright is out of sight
> In the printing business.
> You ne'er can find so bright a mind
> As his'n is.

Ed and Wilbur groaned their appreciation, as they usually did at Paul's far-fetched rhymes or puns; the louder they groaned the better he liked it. Orville said the lines were a touching tribute to his ability—he would leave them on the wall for inspiration.

Paul stood up a few minutes later. "I have to finish collecting for Ma," he said. "Then I have to write two stories for the *Times* over the week end, besides my homework."

"How're you doing in math these days?" Orville asked.

"Ugh!" Paul made a face. "I managed to squeak through algebra with your help, and I'll never know how I got through geometry; but trig!" He rolled his eyes in horror.

"Why did you take it?" asked Wilbur.

"College preparatory," Paul said a little shyly. He hadn't told anyone his dream of going to Harvard. He smiled. "Just in case I get the chance!"

"You'll make it," Orville predicted. "If you get stuck in trig I'll help you."

"Thanks, Orv." Paul wrapped his scarf around his throat and put on the warm woolen gloves Ma had knitted for him. It had begun to snow when he came in, and the big, fleecy flakes were still falling slantwise across the window-panes. Once outside, he didn't hurry, but ambled along through the soft, damp whiteness, enjoying the feel of snow in his face. He took off his gloves and scooped up a hand-ful. Just right for packing. He made several snowballs and smacked them against the tree trunks as he went along. He laughed to himself remembering how he used to sneak out to play in the snow when he was nine or ten, and Ma would always make him come in before he'd half begun to enjoy himself. A few years later he wrote one of his most mischievous poems in dialect about those winter days. He called it "A Grievance."

> W'en de snow's a-fallin'
>   An' de win' is col',
> Mammy 'mence a-callin',
>   Den she 'mence to scol',
> "Lucius Lishy Brackett,
>   Don't you go out do's,
> Button up yo' jacket,
>   Les'n you'll git froze."

> I sit at de windah
>   Lookin' at de groun',
> Nuffin nigh to hindah,
>   Mammy ain' erroun';

Wish't she wouldn' mek me
    Set down in dis chaih;
Pshaw, it wouldn't tek me
    Long to git some aih.

So I jump down nimble
    Ez a boy kin be,
Dough I's all a-trimble
    Feahed someone'll see;
Bet in half a minute
    I fly out de do'
An' I's knee-deep in it,
    Dat dah blessed snow.

Den I hyeah a pattah
    Come acrost de flo'.
Den dey comes a clattah
    At de cabin do';
An' my mammy holler
    Spoilin' all my joy,
"Come in f'om dat waller,
    Don't I see you, boy?"

W'en de snow's a-sievin'
    Down ez soft ez meal,
Whut's de use o' livin'
    'Cept you got de feel
Of de stuff dat's fallin'
    Roun' an' white an' damp,
'Dout some one a-callin',
    "Come in hyeah, you scamp!"

Now, although he was seventeen and a half, Ma still scolded him when he came in, damp and chilled from lingering so long on the way home.

"Smart as you are, seems like you'll never learn that you catch cold quicker'n most boys. I declare, Paul, you don't use good sense sometimes!" She took his wet jacket, with a few star-shaped snowflakes still clinging to it, and hung it over a chair near the woodstove.

Paul laughed at her and told her not to fret, but the next morning he did wake up with a sore throat, and he missed several days of school the following week. He went back but he still had a cough, which he couldn't shake. The trouble with Paul's colds was that they always went into his chest and stayed there. In February, he came down with another one, and this time he was really sick. Ma called the doctor, who prescribed pills and cough medicine, and ordered Paul to stay in bed. With all his running around he had worn himself out, and he had to rest to regain his strength.

After the fever was gone, he read almost all day. Bud brought him books from the school library, so he had a fresh supply two or three times a week; he finished the entire "reading list" in Literature, and went on to other books. He wrote a new poem and a short story, but most of the time he didn't feel well enough to do anything but read. By the third week he was restless and ready to go back, but the doctor thought he should stay home another week. He was not gaining weight the way he should.

The doctor's verdict coming on the Monday Paul had expected to return, sent his spirits down to his toes. He sat listlessly in the carpet-back rocker, watching Ma iron; he didn't even feel like reading. To cheer him up, she told him about a big party they had had once on the Venables' plantation, when "ole man Johnson," dancing with huge Aunt Maria, trying to show how nimble he was at ninety, got so excited he took a great big jump and landed head first in the fireplace! The way Ma described it was so funny Paul had to laugh, picturing the ancient gray-haired grandpa, his face full of ashes and soot, leaping up before the fire had a chance to burn him, and brushing the sparks

out of his hair. And then the "eats" were served right at
that moment or the party might have broken up, Ma went
on to tell, and before she finished naming all the famous
dishes, Paul's mouth was watering. He ate a good lunch
of cornpone and soup although he hadn't had much appetite until then.

In the afternoon, he was beginning to feel bored again,
wishing he were in the *Times* office at school, when a loud
knocking came at the door. Ma opened it, and in trooped
a whole bunch of the boys—Orville, Ezra, Jim Whyte, Bud
and Charley, and a classmate Paul had never known too
well, who was almost as wide as he was tall. It made Paul
so happy to see them all that he blurted out, "Hello, everybody; hello, Fatty!" But "Fatty" didn't seem to mind,
and somehow the expression Paul had given the word was
so comic it struck them all as funny, and they started to
laugh. They laughed and laughed, at nothing at all really,
until they could hardly stop. The whole visit was hilarious,
and the next morning Paul woke up feeling much better.

"Those boys did you more good than a whole bottle of
Dr. Jimson's tonic," Ma said.

She was right, and within a day or two Paul was in class
again, trying to make up the work he had missed. He was
hopelessly behind in math, but way ahead in Literature
because of the reading he had done. He studied hard, and
was soon caught up in everything but the terrible trig.
He decided to ask Orville for the promised help, and went
around to the print shop the next Saturday, only to find
the whole place buzzing. Ed Sines and Orville both hinted
that something big was going to happen, but they were
aggravatingly mysterious about it.

"Can't tell you much till it's settled," Orville said.

"Watch for the April first issue," Ed added.

Wilbur wasn't there, but if he had been Paul wouldn't

have expected any information from him, since he was always close-mouthed anyway. Orville did promise to give Paul a few pointers in trig after school on Monday, but he wouldn't have much time to spare once "It" had taken place, he explained.

Paul soon had his notebook and pencil out, and in a few minutes handed Orville a little sheet of paper on which he had scribbled:

> Come, come assist me, truant Muse!
> For I would sing of the *West Side News*,
> A sheet that's newsy, pure, and bright—
> Whose editor is Orville Wright.
> And by his side another shines
> Whom you shall know as Edwin Sines.
> Now all will buy this sheet, I trust,
> And watch out for their April bust.

His friend was tickled with the rhyme. "We'll use it in the next issue as a teaser," he said.

The great event, when it was finally made known on April 1, was a change in the *West Side News* from a weekly to a daily paper, called the *Item*. And from the day it began, Orville had little time to coach Paul, although he did show him the best way to solve certain problems. The rest of the term Paul struggled by himself, hoping for the best. He was so busy with preparations for graduation, particularly the Central High *Annual*, which included pictures of all the seniors, the faculty, and the organizations, that he couldn't worry about his "worst subject" for long.

One day in May, Captain Stivers called him into the office. "Sit down, Paul," he said with his usual pleasant smile. But his eyes were grave, Paul thought as he took the chair the principal offered. He wondered what the trouble could be.

The Captain was holding some cards in his hand; they had come from the report files in the office, he explained. Paul's grades were all good with one exception, and he hardly needed to mention what it was. "Literature, 97; Chemistry, 81; Latin, 85; and Mathematics . . ." The Captain held up the last card and shook his head. "Failing. I'm afraid you'll have to take it over, Paul."

The room was very quiet for a moment. Then:

"You mean . . . I won't be able to graduate next month." Paul said.

Captain Stivers nodded. "I'm sorry, my boy." He went on to say that the illness had been a real setback, and he hoped that during the summer Paul would grow strong enough so he wouldn't have to be absent as much next winter. He added, turning quickly to a more pleasant topic, that Paul must come to see the fine wood he had found for his violinmaking.

Paul only half-heard him. He stared out of the window at the crab-apple tree in blossom, and saw his dream of college go drifting off beyond the horizon. A whole year more until he graduated! Now he would never get to Harvard.

Once he had accepted the idea of remaining at Central an extra year, Paul went ahead with the plans for the yearbook; the rest of the staff depended on him. He even had his picture taken—he could use it next year, too. After all, he was a senior, and a prominent one. When he posed for the photograph he made sure his coat hung open far enough to show the Philomathean pin on his vest pocket.

And in the fall, from the beginning of the term, Paul was one of the top leaders at Central. He was elected president of Philomathean by unanimous consent, and shortly afterward he was made editor of the *Times*. He was so popular at school Ma said it was a wonder he didn't become a swell-head. The only study he really had to work at was math, but his grades went up in everything when the first-term marks came out. In trig he passed with a comfortable margin, and in Literature he was way ahead of everybody.

He missed Orville and Ezra and some of the others in class, but Bud, Charley and Randy were seniors now, so they and Paul could all graduate together. He usually saw Orville and Ezra on Saturday mornings anyway. He felt as if he were part of the staff at the little newspaper office, since he had been "in" on it from the beginning. (Orville often said the paper couldn't go to press without Paul and Ezra.) The *Item* had been welcomed by the four other dailies when it came out, and it was well received by Dayton readers. The subscription list and the advertising grew steadily; as a result, the job-printing increased by leaps and bounds, until the Wrights decided to move into still larger quarters on Third Street.

When Paul arrived on Saturday morning toward the end of November, boxes stood in the hallway, files were piled in the middle of the office, furniture was stacked ready for the movers, and papers flew all over the place.

"I see you're being evicted," he said.

For answer, Orville thrust some heavy scrapbooks under his arms and asked if he would carry them over to the new offices. When Ezra came a few minutes later, they handed him some of the record books to carry over; Ed and Orville each took some of the files, and the four of them formed a little caravan down the street, joking and calling out comments to each other on the way. Wilbur stayed to supervise the movers, and in a few minutes passed the boys as he was riding beside the driver on the wagon. Hoots and catcalls followed him—why should they walk and he rumble by like a king?

But they were finally at the new shop, and Orville was determined to hang out the sign before they did anything else.

"If you'll just grab my feet, I can lean out the window and fasten it up," he said to Paul and Ezra.

So they each held one of his feet, while he reached out and tied the sign, "Wright Brothers, Printing," to the crossbar above the door. People passing by stared with astonishment at the young man suspended in mid-air between the doorway and the window, but he was unconcerned and so were the boys; they were all enjoying themselves. When the sign was up, they shifted the furniture till it was in exactly the right spots, and began to bring order out of the chaos of moving.

Paul couldn't stay till the job was done, because he had too many other things to do; but on the way home he went down by the river, because an idea had come to him, suddenly, in the midst of the hubbub just now, and he wanted to think it over. He crossed the Dayton View bridge and descended the bank. The water looked murky, reflecting the gray November sky; the dried grasses along the edge were brown, like the bare branches of the trees above; but for once Paul hardly noticed the appearance of his favorite place. This time he was figuring, and it had nothing to do with mathematics. The success of Orville and Wilbur's paper, from the tiny *Midget* to the full-grown daily *Item* had inspired Paul with a plan that had come to him as he was hanging onto Orville's foot and it had almost made him let go. It flashed into his mind like a headline: a newspaper for Negroes—why shouldn't there be such a publication in Dayton, and why shouldn't he start it?

He would be the editor and chief writer; Charley Higgins and Randy could be reporters; Bud was not interested in writing, but maybe he would help bring in subscriptions and ads. The Wright brothers could do the printing—maybe they would give him a special rate. He felt like running back to the shop to talk it over with Orville and Wilbur, but he knew they were in too much of a muddle with the moving. Instead, when he had formulated plans for the staff, and the sort of paper he would publish—a four-page weekly to begin with, containing stories and news items of Dayton's West Side and East End colored neighborhoods—he hurried home to tell Ma.

She thought it might be too much of an undertaking, but she did not discourage him. The way Ma felt was that if Paul wanted to try a new venture like this it was fine, and she wouldn't be the one to put a damper on it.

In the afternoon when his gang came over, he outlined the plan to them; and by evening they were ready to pair off and go around to West Side homes for subscriptions. Paul decided they would have to line up a certain number of subscribers before they could bring out the first issue, and they should have ads, too; but to start off they must have some readers. The families in the neighborhood welcomed the idea of a newspaper for Negroes, and Mr. Finley said he would take a series of ads for his carpet-cleaning business. A couple of days later Paul stopped in to consult the Wright boys, who agreed to do the printing job "on the cuff" until the new weekly began to pay for itself. They both wished Paul luck with the Dayton *Tattler*, the name he had decided to give his little paper.

The first issue came off the press on December 13, 1890, and it contained a variety of news and fiction, all from the same pen—that of Paul Laurence Dunbar, whose name appeared only as "Editor." But those who put the paper to bed knew that the opening installment of a western, "The Gambler," had also been written by the Editor, as well as a little short story called, "His Failure in Arithmetic."

Paul picked out a number of fancy pen names to disguise the authorship of all these stories—Peter Devereux was the one he used most—and he had a great time letting his imagination run on in thinking up plots. A real thriller, "His Bride of the Tomb," began in the third issue; and the young editor had many ideas for more serials to follow. The people who received the Dayton *Tattler* were highly enthusiastic, and eager for more such entertainment.

However, the trouble was that there were not enough of these subscribers, and it was a tough job to get any more. All too few Negroes were "readers," Paul discovered; too few had received the education for reading. And, what was more important to the life of any paper, advertising was almost impossible to sell on a limited publication like the *Tattler*. Poor Mr. Finley was almost alone with his steady ad on the back page.

In spite of all the difficulty, Paul and his staff held on for six issues before the publication folded. They had just about broken even on the venture, but there was little chance of earning money with it, and Paul was not going to run up another bill with the Wright brothers. They had been generous as it was.

"You made a good try, Deac," Orville said sympathetically.

"Thanks," Paul smiled. "It was fun while it lasted!"

He added a copy of each issue to the pile on the parlor table, and turned to the business of preparing for graduation. This time nothing must go wrong. He saw to it that his marks in math remained slightly above passing so there would be no question. Then there was a competition at school for a class poem; the best one would be used as a farewell song, sung by the seniors at graduation exercises. Paul was confident that he could write a good poem, but he wanted it to be the best of those submitted, and he did have several rivals for the honor, students whose pieces he had accepted for the *Times* since he had become editor.

He couldn't be sure that Professor Schweitzer, the music master, would take too kindly to his entry. Paul was a member of the school chorus, not because he had a very good singing voice, but because he liked to let it out. But he did not like the professor's style of presenting the songs, his elaborate arrangements, with extra trills and runs, and fancy cadenzas by the organ in between the verses. Paul preferred the old-fashioned form of singing, the way Ma led them in spirituals—strong, natural tones pouring out, not smothered by squeaks and squawks of solo parts stuck in to make it sound "operatic." He and the professor had had quite a disagreement on this score at the last chorus rehearsal.

"Can't we sing the songs in the old-fashioned way?" he had asked after they had stumbled through a complicated arrangement that the music master evidently considered elegant.

"Herr Dunbar," Professor Schweitzer began in acid tones. (Like the math teacher, he was from the large German population in central Ohio, and had taught in the music department at the University of Cincinnati.) "I haf studied in the conservatory, and haf taken pains to gif you the latest styles in choir zinging. What, may I ask, are your objections to zis?" He tapped the sheet of music on the stand with his baton.

Paul couldn't tell him exactly, because he didn't know much about musical arrangements, but he felt strongly that a simple style was better than a complex one, especially for a high school chorus, and they had argued for some time about it without settling the point. A few days later, the *Times* carried a poem by Paul, written in Hoosier dialect, after the manner of James Whitcomb Riley, the Indiana poet, whose work he admired. He wrote as if he were an old man, thinking back; the opening stanzas stated his views in no uncertain terms:

> You kin talk about yer anthems
>   An' yer arias an' sich,
> An' yer modern choir-singin'
>   That you think so awful rich;
> But you orter heerd us youngsters
>   In the times now far away
> A-singin' o' the ol' tunes
>   In the ol'-fashioned way.
>
> There was some of us sung treble
>   An' a few of us growled bass,
> An' the tide o' song flowed smoothly
>   With its 'comp'niment of grace;
> There was a spirit in that music,
>   An' a kind o' solemn sway,
> A-singin' o' the ol' tunes
>   In the ol'-fashioned way.

The poem was hailed with great glee by the students, particularly those in the chorus; but Paul was certain Professor Schweitzer did not see the humor of it—nor the point. And since he was the sole judge of the verses submitted for the class song, Paul had quite a few qualms about the chances of his poem being chosen. He wished now that he had not been so quick to print "The Old-Fashioned Way."

Toward the middle of May, about the same time Captain Stivers had summoned him the year before, he was called to the principal's office again; and the sight of Professor Schweitzer, seated beside the Captain, didn't make for a feeling of confidence. But this time Captain Stivers' news was good: Paul's poem had been selected for the class song!

"And we will present it in 'the old-fashioned way,'"
Professor Schweitzer added, the ghost of a twinkle in his
eyes.

Paul was surprised, and not a little embarrassed; he had
never expected the music master to give in to his views.
When both men congratulated him, he stammered his
thanks and tried to think of something else to say.

Professor Schweitzer helped him out. "I haf composed
some music for your poem," he said, "and I would like to
go over it with you before we start rehearsals."

Happiness flooding his face, Paul went over the notes
with him; and in a few days he began to hear snatches of
his song hummed through the halls by students who were
rehearsing it for graduation.

The exercises were held at the Opera House, on the evening of June 16, 1891. "Thirty-four young ladies, and
nine young men," as the Dayton *Herald* called them, were
on the platform to receive their diplomas. It was a warm
evening, and Paul, dressed like the other boys in a dark
suit, white shirt and high, tight collar, ran his finger along
the inside of the neckband now and again to get some air.
He had stuck a field daisy in his lapel as he and Ma crossed
the lot on the way to the Third Street horse car. "It's
our class flower," he explained; "only they call it 'mar-
guerite'!" he laughed.

The girls carried bouquets of the flower, to match their
long white dresses, which barely showed their shoetops;
and some of them wore daisies in their hair, too; all of
which lent a festive atmosphere to the stage. Down in the
front row sat Ma, wearing the first new dress she had
bought in years, a smile of proud expectancy on her face.

The program started with an invocation, followed by
speeches—the valedictory address, Captain Stivers' parting
advice to the seniors—and the presentation of diplomas.

Finally the signal Paul had been waiting for came as Professor Schweitzer approached the organ; and the class stood up to sing their farewell song. In the seat next to Ma, a reporter for the Dayton *Herald* wrote: "The beautiful farewell song composed by Paul Laurence Dunbar, colored member of the class, was sung by the graduating class, closing the exercises." If he had looked up, he would have seen the tears of joy shining in Ma's eyes, for she didn't bother to brush them away.

CHAPTER X

The World Outside

GRADUATION BEHIND HIM, and his high school diploma, which Ma framed and hung on the parlor wall, a reality, Paul set out to look for a job, the tide of hope rising high within him. With his record on the *Times*, he should be able to land a newspaper post on one of the four dailies in town. He would try the Dayton *Herald* first, since they had published a number of his poems and knew his work better than the others.

"How do I look?" he asked Ma when he was ready to start out.

She dried her hands, wiping off the suds from the wash tub, and inspected him carefully.

Paul had grown tall in the last two years, she realized
suddenly. She saw before her a slender young man, with
a well-shaped head (ears set close to the sides) and a
thoughtful, even a solemn face; to those who didn't know
him, Paul did look like a deacon. The great dark eyes, the
full lips so firmly set in an expression of strong determina-
tion gave him an air of dignity unusual in a boy of nineteen.
When he smiled, however, the solemnity vanished quicker
than clouds before a sunbeam, and he was more like a
devilish urchin than a church dignitary. His whole face
seemed to glow from the inside when he heard Ma's words:

"You look like a man, Son—an' I know you'll act like
one, too." It was her way of complimenting him, letting
him know that she had confidence in him; and at the same
time preparing him for the struggle he would be up against
in applying for white-collar jobs.

"I hear you, Ma," he said. He gave her a quick hug and
went out the door and down the street at a swinging gait,
his body lithe, his step springy.

When he came into the wide editorial room at the
Herald, where the reporters sat in a long row pounding out
copy, he felt a little nervous. But the managing editor,
whom he asked to see, greeted him kindly and praised his
poems, so Paul had the courage to ask him about getting
on the staff of the paper—he would do anything to start
with; if he couldn't be a cub reporter right away then a
copy boy . . .

The man across the desk stopped him before he went
any further. "I'm afraid we can't take you on in any capac-
ity," he began hesitantly, frowning at the cigar he held
in his hand. "Not that I don't like your work. I think you
have a great deal of ability, and hope you will continue to
write poetry. But I can't hire you. I . . ." He stopped

a moment and then blurted: "It's against the policy of the paper to hire a Negro."

Paul had not expected to be hit so soon. He thought a newspaper would be more enlightened, especially one that had been printing his work right along. He wanted to cry out, "What's the color of my skin got to do with my being a writer?" Instead he said quietly, "I see," and stood up to leave.

"I'm sorry," the editor apologized weakly. "I hope you realize that I cannot go counter to the policies set up by the company. I'll always be glad to publish your verses if you care to go on sending them. . . ."

Paul forced himself to say "Thank you," and made his way out of the office as quickly as possible. The worst part of the turn-down was that the managing editor was genuinely sorry and yet he could do, or would do nothing to change the order of things. Because the Negro had done menial labor before Emancipation, he was expected to go on taking only menial jobs, no matter how much learning he managed to acquire, no matter how much ability he had. At the moment Paul did not figure it out in so many words; he felt it—and he also felt hurt, bewildered, as if someone had struck him when he wasn't looking.

However, Paul wasn't going to be stopped right at the beginning. He went to the other three dailies in town, just to make sure he didn't miss out on anything. The editors all gave him the same story; one of them disguised it a little by saying merely, "We have no openings right now." But he did not suggest that Paul should come back later.

When he came home at dusk, Ma wanted to hear everything that happened, but he didn't care to talk about his experience, not for a while anyway. "No openings right now," was all he told her, repeating the words of the editor at the *World*. He smiled to himself; at least the man had given him a line to use, all unknowingly.

Ma didn't press him with questions. She knew what the answers would be. She had chitt'lins sputtering in the pan, and the cornpone must be just about baked through by now. She opened the oven door, and the warm, fragrant air that drifted out made Paul feel much better. There was poetry in such a moment . . .

> When you set down at de table,
>   Kin' o' weary lak an' sad,
> An' you'se jes' a little tiahed
>   An' purhaps a little mad;
> How yo' gloom tu'ns into gladness,
>   How yo' joy drives out de doubt
> When de oven do' is opened,
>   An' de smell comes po'in' out;
> Why, de 'lectric light o' Heaven
>   Seems to settle on de spot,
> When yo' mammy says de blessin'
>   An' de co'npone's hot.

The next day he went through the want ads, and made a list of all the positions he might possibly fill. He went systematically down the columns; one ad for a clerk turned him down before he had finished reading it. "No colored boy need apply," the wording ran. Paul was boiling mad. "They don't even give you a chance to ask for work!" he exploded to Ma.

But he set out all the same, asking for any sort of office work. The answer was always the same, with slight variations, until it took on the tone of a dirge, sounding over and over in his ears.

"Sorry, nothing for Negroes." "Nothing for Negroes. Sorry." "No, not a Negro, sorry." "Can't employ colored people in office work; too bad." Most of them seemed to regret having to say "no" to Paul. They could see he was well-mannered, soft-spoken, and highly intelligent. Some of them knew about "that Dunbar boy" from his career at Central, and thought he would be worth the chance, but no one wanted to be the first to make such a move.

When you were nineteen, and bursting with ambition, it was hard to believe that people were so narrow-minded and unyielding, even when you heard the same words time after time. Through endless summer days, Paul kept tramping from place to place, hoping he would find some-one with the courage and vision to hire him, no matter what his color.

"I wonder how it would be if I were bright green," he said to Ma. "Think I should paint my face and see what happens?"

She laughed and told him to pack his books and papers before he took such a rash step. They were moving to a smaller house on the edge of town, farther out than they had ever been, and right on the river. The boarder Ma had taken in had become ill and died after a few months, and she had not wanted to rent the extra room again. The little house beside the Miami would be easy to heat in winter; and when they moved in, a few days after Paul had packed his treasures (including the Philodramian dueling-swords), they found the new place breezy and cool in summer. Paul said it was like a country estate, and called it "Riverdale."

He loved being able to look out on the water when he woke up in the morning; and in the evening when he came home after job-hunting all day it was a blessing to sit on the bank in the cool night air. Ma complained of loneliness because they were so far away from the old neighborhood where most of their friends were, but the Whiteline street-car was close by, and on week ends, they had lots of com-pany—everybody wanted to get away from the heat in

town. If Ma wanted to go visiting herself, she could always
hop on the horse car. (Since Paul went in to town every
day, he walked, to save the carefare; and besides, he enjoyed hiking along the road in the "country part" of the
trip.)

He kept on writing whenever he had the chance, late at
night, or sometimes early in the morning, before he started
job-hunting. Or he would spend an hour scribbling as
he sat on the waterfront while Ma fixed supper when he
came home. He longed to have a poem published in *Century*, the leading literary magazine of the day. The dream
was a distant star, but he had hitched his wagon to it when
he had first read the copy his English teacher had brought
into class two years ago, and he was not going to give up
trying to reach his planetary goal.

In the meantime, however, he did have to locate some
kind of work which would bring in a little money regularly every week. He went out to the National Cash
Register Company, where a good many West Side boys
were in the shipping department. There was room for
another hand, the foreman told him; but lifting the heavy
crates in the shipping room was too much for his slight
frame. He was so worn out by the end of a week that he
began to cough again, and Ma insisted that he give up the
job.

"No need to make yourself sick," she said emphatically,
"or you'll be more hindrance than help!"

It was no use knocking on office doors again. Of course
he could always apply for the "dirty-hands" jobs around
town, sweeping floors, clean-up work in hotels, office buildings, and restaurants. But he ran into unexpected opposi-
tion at the employment office, where lines of day-laborers
were waiting for work. They were a seedy-looking lot of
men, who eyed him suspiciously.

They seemed to resent his presence; and one of them, whom Paul remembered seeing at the Lodge theatricals once or twice, asked suddenly, "Ain't you that Dunbar boy who speaks the pieces?"

"Yes, I am," Paul admitted.

"I thought so," was the only comment, but the man's face, and those of the rest, said plainly, "Why don't you find work in your own field? You're only making it harder for us here."

He wanted to explain that white-collar jobs were as impossible for him to secure as for them, but he knew they wouldn't believe him. Their bitter resentment made him realize how helpless they all were. Oh, things were better than they were in Ma's time, before the war, but there was still a long road ahead before equality was anything more than a word in the Constitution. The more people were educated, the sooner it would come about; in another generation or two the difference in color wouldn't matter here, any more than it had at Central, where he had been made editor of the paper and president of Philomathean. He wished he could tell this to the men, could show them that he and they were in the same ditch, but at the moment he felt embarrassed more than anything else, because of the way they stared at him with angry indignation. And after a minute or two, they turned their backs on him, shutting him out.

His appearance was against him with the men who did the hiring, too. "These jobs are not for you," they told him. "Try to find something more suitable."

Paul could almost have laughed, if he hadn't needed work. He was not high enough to wear a white collar, nor low enough to put on work pants, but somewhere in between. Toward the end of summer, he saw an ad for an elevator boy at the Calahan building downtown, and decided to apply.

The building manager was impressed with his neatness and quiet manner. "I think you'll do very well," he said. "Can you start next Monday?" The salary was four dollars a week, he added.

Four dollars; not much, but it was better than nothing, Paul figured, and it would mean a steady income for Ma. She could pay the rent and buy a good bit of food for four dollars. Prices were going up—pork chops were twelve cents a pound—but even so . . .

"I'll take it!" he told the manager. "What time shall I be here Monday morning?"

"Seven o'clock," was the answer. "Now, if you'll just take this home and try it on for size." He handed Paul a suit box, and smiled. "Bring it with you when you come in on Monday. You'll receive instructions on running the elevator then. Good luck!" He held out his hand.

"Thank you, sir." Paul shook hands and left, tucking the long box under his arm.

Later, before Ma's inquiring eyes, he took off the lid. "It may not be a white-collar job, but at least it's more 'suitable'!" he said.

CHAPTER XI

Elevator Boy—and Poet

B-RRIING! the elevator sounded. Paul slid his tablet and pencil on top of the volume of Shakespeare he kept under the tall wooden stool where he sat. He pulled down the lever, closing the doors of the iron cage, which rose on rather creaky chains to the seventh floor.

He picked up two passengers, nodded pleasantly, and took the elevator back down to the main floor. As soon as the people were gone, he reached down and pulled out his blue-lined tablet and pencil, as if he had hardly been interrupted.

"She heedeth not how swift the hours fly," he read over what he had just written, pondering on the next line. He was working on the second stanza of the poem, "October,"

which he had never completed. Usually, when he started
a poem, he finished it right away, but this one he had set
aside when the boys all decided to go to the minstrel show
that night nearly four years ago, and for some reason he
had never gone back to it. He had come across the paper
when he had packed for the moving; and now, when he
discovered he had time to write between trips in the elevator, he dug it up again. He thought for several minutes,
moving his lips silently as he tried out words and ideas.

"But smiles . . . and sings . . . her . . . happy life . . .
'By?'" he wondered. No; it rhymed with "fly" in the line
above, but the meter wasn't right. Anyhow, he would
have to use alternate rhymes in the first half of the stanza,
because he had done it that way in the opening one. He
bit his lower lip, "and sings her happy life . . ."

B-rring! went the bell again. He rode up to the fifth
and down, balancing his pad and pencil on his knee until
he was back by himself. Then he wrote "along," ending
the line to his satisfaction. He murmured the words softly:
"But smiles and sings her happy life along . . ." Yes, it was
right now. He began on the next. "She only sees . . .
above . . . a bright blue . . ." no, that was all wrong.

"Hello, Paul," he heard somebody say, and he looked
away from the tablet to see a little knot of girls coming
toward the elevator—Bessie and Mabel Finley, with
Eugenie Griffin. They had heard he was in the Calahan
building, and stopped by to see him.

"You look pretty slick in your uniform," Bessie said.

"Thank you, ma'am." Paul lifted his cap with the visor
and set it on his head at a rakish angle.

The girls giggled.

"How do you like the job?" Eugenie asked.

"Oh, it has its ups and downs," Paul said carelessly, and
after a moment his little audience squealed at the joke.

"Oh, Paul—still the worst punster in the world!"

"You're a caution, Paul!"

Eugenie asked to see what he was writing, but he wouldn't show her.

"Some day you may read it in a book," he told her, although he had little notion just how and when this would come about.

"Oh, Paul, really?" "Do you mean it?" "When?" They wanted to know, but right then the bell rang again, and when he came down the girls were gone, so he didn't have to answer. He took up the tablet again and worked for nearly half an hour without interruption. Then it was lunch time and he was riding up and down every couple of minutes. When most of the lawyers and insurance men who rented offices had gone out, he left the elevator door open so he could hear the bell, and went around the corner of the lobby to the stairway. Sitting on the lower steps, he ate the sandwich Ma had fixed for him and continued reading the second act of *A Midsummer-Night's Dream*, which he had begun that morning. As soon as he had finished lunch, he walked back to his post, hardly taking his eyes from the page, and was on the wooden stool, still reading, when a lady came in and asked for the "Fourth floor, please."

Paul jumped slightly and looked up. She was well-dressed and very pretty, and she was carrying a parasol to protect her from the bright October sun. She laughed in a friendly way as Paul hurriedly put the book under the stool and pulled down the lever.

"Sorry to interrupt you," she said. "What were you reading that was so absorbing?"

"*Midsummer-Night's Dream.*"

The woman showed surprise. "It's most unusual to find an elevator boy who reads Shakespeare," she commented.

Paul smiled. "I'm really a writer," he told her. Somehow he felt completely at home with the lady. "But writers have to eat, you know."

She nodded understandingly. They were at the fourth floor, but she did not get off right away. She wanted to know what he had written, and when she heard that he had had poems published in the *Herald,* she asked his name.

"So you're Paul Laurence Dunbar!" she exclaimed when she heard it. "Why, I've read your poems in the paper! I thought they were so good I clipped every column that had one of your pieces and pasted it in my scrapbook." She couldn't get over the fact that this was the talented poet she had been wondering about. He was so young!

Paul felt his initial thrill of "recognition" running down his spine. How wonderful it was to learn that people were reading what he wrote! She was Mrs. Frank Conover, she told him. Her husband, he knew, was a prominent lawyer whose offices took up half the fourth floor.

"I have to run now," she said. "But we'll talk more another time—and I'll be following your career, Paul Dunbar."

He thanked her, and went zooming happily down to the main floor. Now to get back to that second stanza. He set down several lines swiftly, inspired by Mrs. Conover's keen interest. By the time people started coming back from lunch he had practically completed the verse. He took it up again when the rush was over, and was pensively chewing the eraser end of the pencil when Ezra Kuhns came up.

His friend had already formed the habit of dropping by and riding up and down in the elevator with Paul. The two discussed all manner of things, as they had done from the earliest debating days; and they would pick out accents and types of people. Paul could tell the difference between the twang of the Hoosier accent around Indianapolis and the slightly broader one from the rural districts that James Whitcomb Riley used in his dialect poems. It was easy to spot a man from southern Illinois or one from Chicago by the way he asked for the floor he wanted. Sometimes the boys singled out Dickens characters in the elevator. Ezra would stand behind Paul, and nudge him when they saw somebody who looked like Mr. Micawber, or Uriah Heep or plodding old Barkus. One day a woman asking for a certain insurance office was so much like Aunt Peggotty they could hardly keep a straight face.

"What's the matter?" Ezra asked now. "Word trouble?"

"Oh, hello, Ez. Yep, you know it!" He nodded in answer to the question. "I'm still wrestling with 'October'— the poem I showed you yesterday."

"Let's hear what you have," Ezra suggested.

"This is the next stanza." He read:

> She heedeth not how swift the hours fly,
> But smiles and sings her happy life along,
> She only sees above a shining sky;
> She only hears the breezes' voice in song.
> Her garments trail the woodlands through,
> And gather pearls of early dew
> That sparkle, till the mischievous sun
> Creeps up and steals them every one.

"Sounds like perfectly good Dunbar to me," Ezra said. "What's wrong?"

"Too many syllables in 'mischievous'," Paul pointed out. "Spoils the meter."

"Let's see. . . ." Ezra began thinking.

A thin-lipped woman entered the elevator. "Seventh floor, please."

Half-way up, Ezra said softly, " 'Devilish'?"

The lady turned around in some surprise. "I beg your pardon?" she asked, coldly disapproving. "Certainly *not!*" she added indignantly.

For a moment the boys looked at each other, puzzled; then they almost burst out laughing, but they held back until Paul announced: "Seventh floor!" and the woman stalked out, casting a backward withering glance at Ezra. All the way down the two word-seekers were in stitches, but Paul finally sobered enough to say that Ezra's choice was still too long; and it was too strong a word, anyhow.

"I guess your passenger thought so, too!" Ezra was hardly able to stop laughing.

But after a few more trips up and down, during which the boys were careful to wait until passengers left the car before they came out with synonyms for "mischievous," they hit upon "roguish," which Paul declared was exactly right.

Ezra, who was helping out in his father's office and studying law at night, was particularly interested in words. "I'd like to be a linquist," he confided to Paul, "but it's not practical."

"Neither is being a poet," Paul said. "Sometimes I wish I'd decided to be a lawyer, just so I'd be sure of a living."

"I have an extra set of law books," Ezra told him, "and a couple of Greek grammars I've been studying. Why don't I bring them here so we can work at them in slack time?"

"Fine," Paul said. And the next day Ezra arrived with an armload of books, which they lined up on the shelf over the radiator in the lobby. He also brought along an extra dictionary for Paul, which went under the stool in the elevator, beside his Shakespeare.

"We'll have a two-man college in the Calahan building,"

Ezra proclaimed as they stood back to view the effect of the books in the bare entrance way.

"Makes the old lobby look like a library," Paul said.

Neither of them, however, had much time to pursue their self-styled "college course." Paul spent a good deal of time studying the copy of *Century* which he borrowed each month from the school library. He went over the stories and poems, and made notes on the sort of thing that the magazine published. If nothing else, he aimed to be accepted for "In Lighter Vein," a section devoted to humorous poetry and anecdote.

The editor of *Century* was Richard Watson Gilder, a literary man with the highest standards; if he accepted an author's work, the person was looked upon as a "recognized" writer. Some of the famous names of the day, appearing regularly, were Charles Dudley Warner, George W. Cable, Joel Chandler Harris, and Hamlin Garland.

Every time Paul completed a poem, or a short story, he submitted the manuscript to *Century* first of all; when they returned it—and so far they always had—he sent it to other publications. His poems began to appear here and there, in places that seemed too remote to win him any recognition, and most of them offered no money; but he had the reward of seeing himself in print, and that alone was compensation for an ardent spirit like Paul's.

In November, the "Negro question" came to the fore once more, and there was talk of sending Negroes to Liberia. "Let them go back where they came from!" people said.

When Paul remembered Ma's story, how close she had come to making the journey that took the lives of so many who attempted it (they had died either crossing the ocean or shortly after reaching Liberia because of conditions there), he was angry at those who suggested such a move after all these years. Negroes born on American soil were American—not Africans. Not only Ma, but Paul's grandmother—"Aunt Becca"—had been born in the United States; and Pa had fought as hard as anyone to keep the country "united," as Mr. Lincoln put it.

Now the southern states were trying to get around the laws giving equality to Negroes. Kentucky passed a "Jim Crow" law, segregating colored from white in streetcars, public buildings, schools and hotels. Reading the news of this legislation in the *Herald*, Paul was outraged at the injustice of it.

"What chance have we got?" he demanded of Charley Higgins. "It's bad enough that prejudice exists—but to make it legal! To separate school children because of the color of their skin!" He thought of the good friends he had made in school—Orville and Ez, and some of the others he might never have known if there had been a "Jim Crow" law in Ohio—and he felt more indignant than ever.

"I know," Charley said. "But we have to do what we can." As a young minister, he was doing his practice preaching at the Eaker Street church and, when he could, he brought problems of the day into his sermons rather than harp on "damnation and salvation."

Frederick Douglass, the famed Negro orator who had been Minister to Haiti for some time, resigned his post to take up the Negro cause in the United States again; the situation was serious. Paul, with his poet's soul, could not help being stirred by these events. During a single morning in the elevator he wrote a fiery poem which he called "O, Mother Race!" pledging his loyalty to his native people. For the first time since he had been writing, he had the desire to be a Negro poet, to be identified as a writer of a downtrodden race, helping to lift it up to its rightful place among mankind. He didn't know yet how he was going to do this; poems like the one he had just finished were an expression of his own deep feelings, but unless a great many people read them, he could go on turning them out for the rest of his life without helping his people one whit.

Somehow, some way, he would have to become a "name" writer. And before that wonderful day could dawn, he would have to *sell* his work, not merely see it in print as "gratis" publication. He must be a "professional" writer, with all that the term implied back of his name.

He decided to try his hand at adventure stories, which newspapers as well as magazines seemed to grab for, as a relief from the grim realities of race riots, depressions and other problems that were hard for readers to face. He saw in an article on writing that a certain author had received $2,500 for a story. Twenty-five hundred dollars! When he figured up the number of years he would have to work as an elevator boy to earn that much money, he unearthed the notebooks he had filled with ideas for stories when he was turning out the *Tattler*, and got busy.

Within a short time, he had written several stories, which he sent to different places. Every night he hurried home from work with the same question: "Any mail, Ma?"

Ma either shook her head or she would silently hand him a fat envelope, which meant that a story had been returned. But he didn't give up; as soon as a manuscript came back, he sent it some place else; and in the meantime he started fresh ones, or penned a new poem to give himself heart.

One day in April, he left the Calahan building with the sensation that something good was about to happen. He leaped across the puddles from a recent shower, their reflection of the spring sky like pale blue patches on the pavement. (Dayton's streets had only been paved a few years; and it was still a pleasure not to sink ankle deep in mud on the corner of Main and Fifth; to see, instead of soupy dirt, churned up by carriage wheels, the smooth shine of cobblestones beneath the wetness.) All the way home he had the feeling of being pulled along by some outside force that whispered, "Run! See what is waiting for you."

He was almost breathless by the time he arrived at "Riverdale," and before the door had closed behind him, he shot out the inevitable, "Any mail, Ma?"

As she had done so often before, she handed him a thick envelope without speaking. What was there to say? She knew what would be inside and so did Paul.

"Is this all?" Paul asked with deep disappointment. His hunch must have been wrong.

"That's it, Son," Ma said with compassionate feeling.

He weighed the package. It was from the Kellogg Syndicate in Chicago. He had sent in two stories, the second shortly after the first because he couldn't wait for a report, even though he knew it was not a wise policy to pelt a publisher with a second manuscript while he was considering one. He tried to guess, from the weight, which story this was—not heavy enough to be *The Tenderfoot* (the first he had submitted), he thought—but still, he couldn't tell. The envelope certainly wasn't thick enough to contain both stories.

"What are you hefting it for?" Ma finally asked impatiently.

Paul laughed. It was silly to go on conjecturing. He ripped open the flap. Something narrow and gray slipped to the floor. He bent over to pick it up, and let out a whoop: "Ma! Look, Ma—a check!" He waved it in front of her eyes like a flag.

Ma was as overjoyed as he, but she inquired practically: "For how much?"

"Oh." He was so excited he hadn't even noticed . . .

well, the amount, when the figures settled down, was six
dollars. A long way from twenty-five hundred, but Paul
didn't stop to calculate the difference. There was a letter
attached to the returned manuscript.

"At present we are overstocked," it said, "but we are
buying *The Tenderfoot*." . . . So he had been right in his
guess. They had taken the first story he sent—and had accepted it even though they were "overstocked." They
must like his work very much.

He was so elated he could scarcely eat supper, and he
felt like a completely different being from the elevator boy
who came home and sat down at Ma's kitchen table every
night. Inside of a few seconds, a small gray slip of paper
had changed him from a struggling amateur to a firm professional. Never mind how small the sum he had received
(at that, it was as much as he earned in a week and a half
at the Calahan building); the important fact was that he
had at last been paid for his talents, and this gave him the
right to go on developing them.

The next day he started another story, a western this
time; and a few weeks later the Kellogg Syndicate pur-
chased it. In a letter accompanying the check, the editor
spoke of publication plans for *The Tenderfoot* as well as
the present manuscript, *Little Billy*. Both would be illustrated by the same artist, with "decorations" at the beginning and end.

When Paul's copies came, he decided to start a scrapbook. He brought home a catalog of the American Screw
Company some salesman had left in the elevator, and pasted
his clippings over the products listed on its pages. He had
several copies of each story, because the Syndicate included
a good many papers; the publishing house was the first of its
kind, and had been started during the war to make for a
faster, wider distribution of news bulletins.

Paul naturally did not receive copies of all the papers in which his work appeared, but there was one from Cincinnati; and from Chicago, where the Kellogg office was located, an issue of the Chicago *News Record* arrived, carrying *The Tenderfoot*. He decided to try sending some of his poems to them when he saw a poetry column like the *Herald*'s on the back page. (The Syndicate handled only stories.) And the Chicago paper not only printed his work, but paid him for it. He had more and more clippings to paste in his catalog-scrapbook. He did not bother with sorting them out or dating them; and sometimes he cut the paper so that the title was missing. In later years, biographers who did research on Paul Dunbar would have a hard time finding out when and where his pieces had been published in those early days; but he was not thinking about posterity when he sat, with Ma's old sewing shears, a pot of flour-and-water paste, and the bulky catalog in front of him, cutting out columns, slapping "goo" on the back, and slamming them on the page with his fist.

Late in June, as he was bent over his notebook in the elevator one morning, his Senior-year English teacher at Central, Mrs. Helen Truesdell, came rushing in to ask whether Paul could deliver the welcoming speech to the Western Writers' Association, which was holding its annual conference at the Opera House beginning June 27. (That was only three days away, he knew, because it was his birthday.)

"I realize this is very short notice," the teacher apologized, "but we didn't receive word that the conference would be here until a few days ago. We feel that you are more representative than any of the Dayton members; and you always were so clever at turning out a last-minute assignment."

Paul was overwhelmed by the teacher's confidence in

his ability, but his head was in a whirl. They were asking
him to give the welcoming speech to an assembly of full-
fledged writers! What would he say? How could he leave
the elevator that long? Yet in spite of all the snags he
might hit, he was delighted to oblige Mrs. Truesdell, and
set about preparing his "speech." Halfway through, a
sudden idea came to him, and he started all over. He would
write the address in verse!

He arranged with the building manager to go off duty
for an hour or so on the day the conference opened, and
reached the Opera House just in time to hear the president
give a few opening remarks, after which the man announced, "Mr. Paul Laurence Dunbar will present the welcome address on behalf of the Dayton members."

A buzz went over the audience as Paul made his way up
the aisle to the platform. Such a young man—a boy, really
—and no one outside of the Dayton members knew his
work. He bowed briefly, and began to read his long poem
of welcome. It was a warm day, hot and humid as June
can often be; the female members of the Association had
been wielding their fans vigorously against the heat of the
hall; but as Paul began to read in his rich low voice, the
flutter of fans ceased. Ladies leaned forward in their seats,
and men stopped rustling their programs. Here was a very
good poem—and so dramatically delivered! When he
finished, Paul received a burst of applause. He smiled and
bowed, happy that his poem had been so well received.
Then he made a dash for the backstage exit of the Opera
House—he was due at the Calahan Building in ten minutes!

After he left, the president explained that he had just
learned (through Paul's teacher, who whispered the information in his ear as Paul was leaving) that the poem
recited by the young man had also been written by him, and
that he was one of Dayton's most promising poets. Now

the applause was thundering, but Paul was not there to hear it.

He was back at the Calahan building, taking passengers up and down; up and down; up and down again. . . .

The next day, three of the men from the Association went to seek out the young writer who had created such a sensation at the opening session of their conference. They found him on the stairway during lunch hour; he was busy jotting down notes for a new poem with one hand and nibbling at an apple he held in the other; he was so engrossed he didn't even hear them approaching.

"Paul Laurence Dunbar?" one of them asked, and he looked up with a start.

"That's right." His eyes were puzzled as he rose.

"Permit me to introduce myself," the man began. "I'm Dr. J. N. Matthews, from the Western Writers' Association."

"Oh!" A broad smile spread over Paul's face. "How do you do?"

"And these are my colleagues. . . ."

Bb-rring! went the elevator bell.

"Excuse me," Paul apologized, burning with embarrassment. "I'll be right back." In two minutes he was with them again. "I'm sorry," he began, but Dr. Matthews waved his apologies away and introduced the two other gentlemen.

"We came to congratulate you on the excellent poem you read yesterday," Dr. Matthews went on. "None of us knew until after you had gone that you were the author."

"I'm glad you enjoyed it," Paul said simply.

"Such a novel idea, to give the welcome address in lyric form," one of the other men took up the conversation. "Have you written much poetry?"

Bhrriinnggg! went the elevator bell. Some passenger was getting impatient.

"Excuse me." Paul left on the run.

When he returned, they had no sooner begun to talk than the bell sounded a third time! The situation struck Paul as funny by now; he broke down and laughed, forgetting his embarrassment. "I'm afraid we'll never finish our conversation here," he said, extending his arm, palm open, in the direction of the elevator. "May I give you a lift?" he invited them.

The men laughed—the young poet was witty as well as wise. Two of them had committee meetings to attend, but Dr. Matthews stayed to ride up and down in the elevator with Paul, talking of poets and poetry in general, of Paul's work in particular. He asked to see more of the pieces which had been published; and before he left he invited Paul to attend the closing session of the conference the next day.

"We would like to have you read several of your poems," he said, "if you can arrange to do so."

Paul's eyes twinkled. "I believe I can manage it."

This time the members of the Western Writers' Association accorded him a real ovation when he ascended the platform; reporters in the audience took note of the reception he was given before he read and after he had finished, when the applause was deafening. The story appeared in all the Dayton papers, and Paul had a good many more clippings for his scrapbook. By the close of the conference, he had been invited to become a member of the Association; and Dr. Matthews said he was going to write a letter about Paul for a chain of newspapers.

"I think the world should know about you," he said. "I'm sure your work will speak for itself in time, but it won't do any harm to hasten the process with a little publicity." He smiled.

Paul hardly knew how to thank him. At the moment, he said little, but he knew the doctor understood when they shook hands. Later, when he received a copy of one of the papers carrying the "Letter," he sat down and put his gratitude in a poem, "To Dr. J. N. Matthews."

The glamor of the conference was over, the routine of Paul's job set in once more.

"Third floor."

"Fourth floor."

"Fifth floor."

"Main floor."

Pull the lever, close the door. . . .

Then it was slack, and he could take up his true work. One of the discussions he had heard, in part, at the last session dealt with the use of dialect in both prose and poetry. The popularity of the writing of James Whitcomb Riley, Joel Chandler Harris and Ruth McEnery Stuart was examined by members who were anxious for wider circulation of their work. Why was dialect so popular? What made it attractive to millions of readers?

Paul set about examing Riley's poems closely. He found that they had a homespun quality; they combined humor and gentle irony with a touch of philosophy, all in the framework of Hoosier speech, rhyme, and metre. They looked into human frailties, and spoke in familiar terms. They portrayed lowly people, lovable people: "Little Orphan Annie," "The Raggedy Man."

He crinkled his eyes, thinking: why shouldn't he, Paul Dunbar, employ Negro dialect in the same way? He seldom spoke it himself, but he had heard plenty from Ma, her relatives, and old friends. He made a point of listening to it closely at Lodge meetings and family reunions, where old stories were told. He went to visit his Aunt Elizabeth, Dora Burton's mother, one night after work. Some of the old East End families who lived in the neighborhood spoke nothing but "plantation talk."

He began writing poetry in Negro dialect, probably the first of his people to do so. Joel Chandler Harris, with his famous "Uncle Remus" legends, and short-story writer Ruth Stuart were both white; so were one of two others who had won their reputations with Negro dialect. And all of them were principally prose writers, not poets. Paul liked to try stories occasionally, too; and since his first sales were in that form, he must have some talent for it, but he thought of himself mainly as a poet.

One of his earliest pieces was "A Banjo Song," which caught the melody and the spirit of the speech he had so often heard. There were eight stanzas, the first and last of which read:

> Oh, dere's lots o' keer an' trouble
>   In dis world to swaller down;
> An' ol' Sorrer's purty lively
>   In her way o' gittin' roun'.
> Yet dere's times when I furgit 'em,—
>   Aches an' pains an' troubles all,—
> An' it's when I tek at ebenin'
>   My ol' banjo f'om de wall.
>
> Now, de blessed little angels
>   Up in heaben, we are told,
> Don't do nothin' all dere lifetime
>   'Ceptin' play on ha'ps o' gold.
> Now I think heaben'd be mo' homelike
>   Ef we'd hyeah some music fall
> F'om a real ol'-fashioned banjo,
>   Like dat one upon de wall.

The poem sold on its first trip out, to the Chicago *News Record*.

Other dialect pieces he tried were taken quickly, too, and there were requests for more. Paul was amazed, and Ma was puzzled.

"What beats me," she said, "is that all the high-soundin' words don't amount to a hoot, moneywise, an' the old plantation talk sells faster'n hotcakes!"

Paul chuckled. "It beats me, too, Ma," he said. "But I guess for a while I'd better go on dishing up hotcakes!"

CHAPTER XII

One Scrumptious Time

DR. MATTHEWS' LETTER, which had been printed in a number of newspapers, finally found its way into the small weekly published in the neighborhood of Riley's country home in Indiana. And one evening when Paul came from the Calahan building, Ma handed him an envelope bearing an Indiana postmark.

"Who do you s'pose is writing to me from Indiana?" Paul wondered.

"Best way to find out is to open it," Ma said drily.

The letter was from James Whitcomb Riley himself! He had seen Dr. Matthews' piece about Paul, and since he had been noticing the young man's poems here and there, he wanted to urge Paul to keep on with his writing career. The letter was full of kindly encouragement, and was all Paul needed to send him onward. At almost twenty, he trembled a little, to think that a well-known established author like James Whitcomb Riley would take the trouble to write to him, Paul Dunbar, an unknown struggling beginner. Still, the very fact that he had received such a letter was a sign that he was creeping ahead, slowly but surely. He was determined that nothing should stop him.

He wrote constantly in the Calahan building. Ezra's law books gathered dust on the shelf above the radiator because Paul's head was full of words far removed from legal phraseology, and he must get them all down. Early in September he was in the throes of composing a rollicking lyric called "The Cornstalk Fiddle," in which he pictured the lively spirit of a mid-western country dance he had attended in one of the Darke County villages near Dayton. As he wrote he could hear the "scrape, scrape, scrape" of the twangy fiddle, and the beat of the feet on the floor of the barn where the dance was held.

He wondered momentarily whatever became of the girl he had taken to that dance—for Paul had a different girl every week, and some of them he hardly saw more than once. He was too taken up with his writing to bother with girls much, and he had no money to spend on "treats" for a steady girl. His salary, padded occasionally by a blessed manuscript check, was just about enough to see him through each week. Ma was not old in years, but she was beginning to feel worked out from the rough labor she had done since the early days of her life. She could not finish as many bundles of laundry in a week as she used to do. She relied on Paul's salary to take care of the major part of their expenses.

"Hello, Paul!" "How's the poet?" "The bard of 'naughty' '90!" A chorus of familiar voices sounded in his ears.

He looked up to see a group of his old classmates coming

in—Orville and Ezra, Jim Whyte, Robert LaRue, Ernie Blumenschtein and one or two others. He was not too surprised to see them; the class he had been in before his failure in mathematics was holding a reunion this fall and he supposed the boys were on a committee planning some entertainment for the event. But the request they made was quite different from what he had expected. They told him now that Old Central was merging with the new high school, Steele, recently completed, and they wanted him to write a poem to fit the circumstance.

"You know—something like an 'alma mater' serenade, only . . ." LaRue began.

"I get it," Paul smiled. "Our old 'soul-mother' has gone and married, had her face lifted and her skirts shortened."

"That's the idea!" Orville nodded. "Write it on the lighter side."

"I will," Paul assured them. "Don't worry."

He had only a little over a week to work on the poem, but he was ready with a freshly written copy of it the day of the reunion and dedication exercises in the new school. Captain Stivers, who introduced Paul, said that all during his years at Old Central he showed signs of becoming a recognized writer some day. "He was as much ahead in Literature as he was behind in math," the Captain told the audience, and Paul laughed along with everybody else. He had no regrets any more about the extra year he had had to spend at Central, especially since the old school was gone forever, and the memories of that final year were among the best he had of his school days.

He read his tribute to the abandoned alma mater with exactly the right blending of sentiment and satire in his voice to match the words. The students, both graduates and under-classmen, laughed at his lines and loved them. Afterward he received congratulations from scores of them;

many asked when he was going to have a book published. He left the auditorium with a whole bunch of former schoolmates, but in the end he and Orville were walking home together—just as they used to—only now Orville was going to the printing office for a while, and Paul would be taking the Whiteline out home.

"Why don't you have a book published, Paul?" Orville asked him suddenly. "Collect a batch of your poems and put them between covers."

Paul merely looked at him.

He stared back seriously. "I'm not joking; I mean it."

"Oh, come on, Orv!" Paul said. "Who would publish a whole book of my stuff?"

"You could find somebody; if I had the proper press I would." The Wrights had given up their paper, and were doing only job printing. He thought a minute. "What about the United Brethren Publishing House?" he suggested. "They put out a lot of things besides religious books."

A light was beginning to shine in Paul's eyes. "Do you really think they might bring out a book of poetry, Orv? *My* poetry?" he asked.

"Why not?" Orville demanded. "At least you could see them."

"I wouldn't know how to go about it." For some reason, Paul was seized with shyness when he thought about showing his work himself; when you mailed a manuscript in, the idea of exposing it to critical eyes didn't seem so personal.

"Just walk in and talk to the business manager, Mr. Blocher," Orville told him. "You can mention my father's name; after all, he's a U.B. bishop now." He smiled.

Paul began to feel enthusiastic. Besides Bishop Wright, he knew another clergyman connected with the publishing

house, whom he had met through Reverend Butler. All the
way home, after Orville had left, he mulled over the project. He would go through his papers from the earliest
days of his writing until the present, and he would pick
out the best. By the time he jumped off the horse car, he
had decided to start going through the pile of papers right
away.

He made straight for the parlor table when he came in
the front door; he and Ma still kept putting his papers in
the same place, even though the pile had grown quite
unwieldy of late. But today *the table was empty!* He
stared unbelieving at the shiny surface which Ma had
evidently polished with beeswax. And what had she done
with the papers? He looked frantically under the table,
in the sideboard drawers. . . .

"Ma! Oh, Ma!" he called in a loud voice, trying to be
calm. "Where are all my papers?"

"You'll find 'em under the kitchen-safe, in a grocery
box," she called back. "The pile was growin' too high for
the table."

But Paul was already on his knees, poking his head under
the safe. There was the grocery carton. He drew it out,
and saw that Ma had neatly stacked everything and put
his scrapbook on top.

"I might've known you'd ask for those soon's I decided
to clear 'em away," she said, sticking her head in the
doorway. "What did you want 'em for now, Son?"

"Oh, Ma," Paul told her confidently, "I'm going to have
a book published!"

"When? How?" Ma folded her arms across her breast,
ready to listen.

"Well—at least I hope so," Paul amended. He went on
to tell her of Orville's suggestion and his own plans. If

Ma had her doubts about his chances of success, she didn't voice them, but, as usual, encouraged him to try.

He spent several evenings picking and choosing, selecting only those poems he considered worthy of putting in a book. In all, he had a sheaf of fifty-six poems by the time he had finished. Included were early ones like the Easter ode, and "On the River," on up to some of the dialect pieces he had been turning out—"A Banjo Song," "Goin' Back" (about an old ex-slave returning to his home in Kentucky), and a number of others. He changed the title of "O, Mother Race" to "Ode to Ethiopia," and altered a word here and there. He felt that the serious poems were stronger than the humorous and dialect pieces. The lesser ones were like ivy twined around a tree trunk—and there was his title: *Oak and Ivy*, he called his book.

He was so keyed up he could scarcely go to sleep the night he completed his manuscript. The package on the bureau top seemed to be alive, resting there in the moonlight that came through the window. He kept watching it, half-fearfully, wondering what its fate would be.

On his lunch hour the next day he hurried over to the United Brethren publishing office and courageously asked for the clergyman he knew. Unfortunately, the man was out of town, and Mr. Blocher, the business manager, was too rushed to give Paul much time.

"I'm afraid you've come to the wrong house," he said. He thumbed through the pages briefly. "Your little manuscript appears to contain material for an attractive volume, but we rarely publish poetry, and almost never take on unsolicited work."

"Oh." Paul looked so disappointed, Mr. Blocher felt he must soften the blow.

"Now, if you were willing to pay the publishing costs,

we could bring out your book, but that is the only basis on which I would consider doing it."

"How much would it be?" Paul asked doubtfully.

Mr. Blocher told him he would have to see the foreman about prices, and showed him where he could find the man, who proved to be more curt and abrupt than the business manager.

"I can't take time to figure publishing costs to the penny," he said. "But it would come to a minimum of $125, payable in advance."

A hundred and twenty-five dollars! Paul would have to work months before he made that amount, and he could never raise the money outside; where could he go for such a staggering sum?

"If you could let me have the book published on credit," he began, "I could pay you back a little at a time."

"No, indeed. You must realize that we can't give credit to a whippersnapper like you without a penny to his name. Our policy in this is inflexible; immediate payment or no publication." He dismissed Paul by turning away to talk to the linotype man.

Paul stumbled slowly toward the door. On the way out, he had to pass Mr. Blocher's desk, and the business manager, seeing his dejected face, asked, "What's the matter, my boy?"

"Oh," Paul burst out, "the foreman told me it would cost $125 to print my book, and he won't trust me for the money."

Mr. Blocher, who knew Paul's work slightly from the poems published in the *Herald*, seemed to be considering the possibilities of the case. "Let me see those poems again," he said suddenly.

"Yes, sir!" Paul dropped the manuscript on the desk like lightning.

Several tense moments went by while Mr. Blocher flipped over the pages, stopping to read here and there. "Some of these are very good," he said at last. "Tell me, if I put up the $125 in advance, do you think you could line up enough subscriptions for the book to pay me back when it comes out?"

"Yes, *sir!*" Paul exclaimed again, this time with a happy grin stretching across his face.

"Very well, get busy!" Mr. Blocher laughed. "You leave this with me," he rested his hand on the manuscript, "and come back in a few days to discuss details of the publication."

Paul did not exactly walk, but rather was wafted back to the Calahan building on wings of joy. He still had a few minutes of his lunch hour left. He took a sheet of his blue-lined tablet paper, and headed it "Subscription List for *Oak and Ivy*." He could probably get lots of orders for his book right there in the building, and he wanted to be prepared.

Mrs. Conover was his first customer. She was delighted to hear of his good fortune, and amazed at his spirit in going out and securing a publisher on his own. Not many young men of twenty in his position would show that much gumption!

"I want to order five copies," she said. "I think your book will make a lovely Christmas present for some of my friends. It will be out in time for Christmas, won't it?" she asked as an afterthought.

"Gee, I don't know the publication date yet!" Paul confessed, and they had to laugh.

He learned the answer to the question at his next interview with Mr. Blocher. The list price of *Oak and Ivy* was set at one dollar per copy; and the publishers hoped to bring the book out in time for the holidays, but they could not promise.

"However, I'll do all I can for you," the business manager assured him.

Paul thanked him, but left the office with the feeling that the question was still up in the air. In spite of the uncertainty over the date, he took orders at a great rate now that the facts were settled. Mrs. Conover told her husband to pass the word of Paul's book among the other lawyers in the building, and a good many of the tenants signed for copies.

Ezra, who was among the first of Paul's friends to put his name on the list, suggested that Paul put up a subscription sheet on the bulletin board at Steele. "You might as well have the support of the students at our new-old alma mater," he said practically, "and if you like I'll arrange it for you."

Some of the seniors had known Paul when they were freshmen, and a great many of the undergraduates knew about him from the teachers. Before long, the list of subscribers grew until there were nearly enough names to cover Mr. Blocher's investment. Bud, Charley, and Randy signed up people in their neighborhoods. The girls, stopping by the Calahan building, were all agog at the idea of Paul's book.

"Do say it will be out in time for Christmas, Paul," said Eugenie Griffin. "I'm going to send one to Lily Hill." She giggled. Lily had moved to Cincinnati after graduation and Eugenie wanted her to know of the excitement she was missing in Dayton.

But he still couldn't tell any one for sure when the book

would be out, because from day to day it became more uncertain.

"Just to play safe, we'd better put an 1893 date on the flyleaf," Mr. Blocher told Paul the third week in December.

And then, on a snowy day just before Christmas, a messenger from the United Brethren Publishing Company delivered two cartons of books to Paul's house. He was at work, but Ma answered the door.

"Books for Mr. Paul Dunbar," the messenger said. "Does he live here?"

"That's right," Ma said. She took the books, and signed for them, her hand not quite steady, holding the pencil.

"Say, what is this Mr. Dunbar?" the man asked curiously. "A lawyer or a preacher or something?"

"Neither one," Ma answered. "He's just an elevator boy —and a poet."

When Paul came home from work, she thrust one of the packages into his hands almost before he closed the door. "I could hardly keep from opening it!" she said.

Without taking off his wraps, he ripped open the top. He was trembling so with excitement he could scarcely pick up the first copy. The books were bound in plain covers, some brown, some red, some blue. The title, *Oak and Ivy*, was stamped on in gold letters, with a gold scroll underneath.

"Where's your name?" Ma demanded, looking over Paul's shoulder.

"Wait a minute." He opened the book to the title page. There it was: OAK AND IVY by Paul Dunbar. The date on the page was 1893, not 1892 as it should have been, because no one thought the books would be ready in time for Christmas. After the title page came the dedication, which Paul held up for Ma to read:

To Her
who has ever been
my guide, teacher, and inspiration
My Mother
this little volume is
affectionately inscribed

All those who had signed for a copy of *Oak and Ivy* were happy to pay for it, and some, like Mrs. Conover, ordered more. Paul kept a stack of them at the Calahan building, and people came in to buy them. One purchaser complained, weighing the volume in his hand, "Mighty little book to sell for a dollar."

But Paul answered smiling, as he folded the man's bill, "A book sells on its merits, sir, not on its size."

Three days after publication Paul had sold eighty-five copies of the "little book"; and two weeks later he was able to pay Mr. Blocher the entire sum he had guaranteed: one hundred and twenty-five dollars.

There was money left over besides. The night before Christmas Paul came home loaded with groceries for the grandest dinner Ma had ever dreamed about. There were also a present or two, hidden away at the bottom of the bag. They had never had such a Christmas as this one.

"We simply had one scrumptious time!" Paul always said happily when he told people about that memorable celebration.

CHAPTER XIII

Fame and Fair

THE SALE from his first book gave Paul the courage to take another plunge. He bought a house for Ma. Or rather, he made arrangements to buy it; all the *Oak and Ivy* earnings went into the down payment, and he took out a mortgage for the rest, which he could pay off monthly at a rate that came to no more than the rent he had been meeting at Riverdale.

He and Ma together picked out their new home, which was at 140 Ziegler Street, close to the center of town. ("We've been stuck away from everybody long enough!" Ma decided.) Yet the place was not hemmed in, by any means—a large pleasant yard, with space for Ma's chickens and a garden, surrounded the two-story frame house. Snowball bushes, roses and lilacs leaned against a white picket fence. "This one has a *homey* look," Ma said, and that settled it. Paul went to see the building and loan company the next day, and by the first of February they had moved into their first real home.

Paul began to realize in other ways the rewards of having his book published. Requests for recitals began to come from Indiana and the bigger cities in Ohio as well as the small towns around Dayton. Nearly every week end found him keeping an engagement to read his poems before good-sized audiences; they usually paid little more than his traveling expenses, and sometimes not that much, but he was gaining a reputation, winning a name for himself and his poetry. The value of small fame was not to be sneezed at, he told Ma, who worried about the time and energy he put in for such measly returns. Big names grew out of little ones, and although his might be undersized now, the readings would help to give it stature. Besides, he thoroughly enjoyed performing in front of an audience, receiving the applause, which was always hearty, and watching for reviews in the papers the next day.

In Richmond, Indiana, where he was called back several times for curtain calls at his fourth engagement in the city, sometime in March, the story in the *Palladium* read: "An appreciative crowd of Richmond's best citizens were charmingly entertained last night by readings of his original poems by Paul Laurence Dunbar. For an hour he held his audience in delicious thrall, their delight being frequently evinced by loud and prolonged applause." The *Independent* also carried a favorable review; and the secretary of the YMCA, where he spoke, gave Paul a letter of recommendation which he could use to line up more recitals.

The speaking dates did not stop the young poet from writing. During his short stay in Richmond, he turned

out one of the longest poems he had ever written; he wrote
it in Hoosier dialect, and called it "The Rivals," since he
was telling the humorous story of two suitors for a lady's
hand.

Writing, to Paul, was as necessary as breathing; he could
not do one without the other.

Among the people to whom Mrs. Conover had sent a
copy of *Oak and Ivy* for Christmas was a young lawyer
in Toledo, a Mr. Charles Thatcher. He was so impressed
with the poems that he wrote a letter asking for more
information about the author. Paul sent an answer right
away, from his stool in the elevator, mentioning his occupa-
tion, and stating the fact that he frequently gave readings
of his poetry. He was going to Detroit around the middle
of April to appear in some Negro churches there, and he
hoped to get other engagements in the neighborhood. Mr.
Thatcher wrote back by return mail: "Please stop off in
Toledo on your way to Detroit."

Paul was not one to hesitate about accepting such invitations. Whatever came of them was worthwhile, and
if nothing did—well, he had little to lose by trying! As he
stepped from the train at the Cherry Street station on that
mild April day, he had no idea what an important part
Toledo was going to play in shaping his career. To begin
with, he didn't even know how to get to Mr. Thatcher's
office. It was only a few blocks down the street, in the
Summit-Cherry building, the porter told him.

This seemed to be a bustling industrial town, he thought
as he walked along; the streets were lined with small business shops, and dozens of delivery wagons went by in both
directions on either side of the brand new trolley cars
Toledo was trying out. Horses whinnied and shied when
the noisy cars passed; it was a wonder the drivers didn't

have a runaway every few minutes! Paul was relieved when he reached the office building.

Mr. Thatcher proved to be the friendly, warm, decisive person his letters had promised. He was full of praise for *Oak and Ivy*. ("I've recommended it to all my friends," he said.) Paul did not have much time to spend with the young, good-looking lawyer, but before he left to catch the train for Detroit, Mr. Thatcher sent his hopes soaring with plans for a possible recital in Toledo "soon."

"Soon" turned out to be the next day, when Paul received a telegram in Detroit asking him to stop on his way home for a recital at the newly formed West End Club, a literary society in Toledo. Mr. Thatcher was a fast worker! As soon as his Detroit program was over, Paul prepared for the recital at the West End Club. He would provide his listeners with lively entertainment, the way he had in Richmond. He included "The Rivals" and several other new dialect poems; they always made a hit.

Mr. Thatcher picked him up at the depot with his horse and buggy, and they drove out to the West End, through the tree-lined streets of Toledo's new fashionable neighborhood to the clubrooms. This would be a far different audience from those Paul had just spoken to in Detroit. He was sure he had chosen the right sort of program. Mr. Thatcher explained as they were going in that Paul would follow the main speaker, a Dr. Chapman, one of the members who had recently returned from a trip through several southern states, and was going to deliver a paper on "The Negro in the South."

"My committee is counting on you to provide the lighter side of the program," he said. "I don't imagine the doctor's paper will be especially entertaining!" He smiled, and whispered, as they slipped into the hall, "We're the only ones who know you're going to appear."

The room was well filled, and the president was introducing Dr. Chapman, so they took seats near the door in the back. The doctor smoothed out his papers, passed his hand over his hair, and began to read. Paul was hoping to hear some comment about southern Negroes which he could refer to in the opening remarks that he, a northern Negro, had planned to make. Instead of this, he was horrified to hear the speaker denounce the Negro in the South! "Lazy . . . shiftless . . . incapable of benefiting by education . . . prefers to remain ignorant . . ." Those were the words used to describe the Negro. Paul felt sick, his head swam.

Vaguely, through the waves of his anger, he heard his name brought into the false picture the man was painting. What was he saying . . . "Paul Dunbar, the Dayton poet . . . an exception . . . a freak of nature. His poems are no proof that Negroes are teachable . . ."

The doctor then went on to tell of the living conditions of the Negro in the South, but in Paul's ears the rest of the speech was drowned by the sea of protest rising in his mind against the slur cast on the Negro's native intelligence. He was so angry he could hardly think. Not "teachable"! Look at Bud—apprenticed to Dr. Reeve, expecting to go to medical school in the fall! And what about Charley, a full-fledged minister now? And Randy, studying law in night school? What about the great names in Negro history, men like Frederick Douglass, who had taught themselves and, against all odds, became educated men? Not teachable!

Sedate applause told him the doctor had finished his paper. Mr. Thatcher nudged him as the president announced with embarrassment that Paul Dunbar had graciously consented to read some of his "own compositions" to the members. A murmur went over the audience

—some of them turned quickly to look at Dr. Chapman, curious to see his reaction, but most of them watched expectantly as Paul walked up the aisle and mounted the steps to the stage. He was scarcely aware of the stir; he was too intent on what he had to do.

He placed his copy of *Oak and Ivy* on the podium, and opened it to an unmarked page. He made no preliminary remarks, and when he spoke, his voice was low and tense with feeling: "I shall give you first a poem I had not intended to recite this evening when I arrived; it is called, 'Ode to Ethiopia.'"

The people before him were suddenly still, hushed by his tone. And they were held, listening almost in a trance to the sonorous lines. There was no doubt that they understood why he had suddenly decided to read this poem, especially when he came to the words that told of the Negroes' accomplishments:

> They tread the fields where honour calls;
> Their voices sound through senate halls
> In majesty and power.
> To right they cling; the hymns they sing
> Up to the skies in beauty ring,
> And bolder grow each hour.
>
> Be proud, my Race, in mind and soul;
> Thy name is writ on Glory's scroll
> In characters of fire.
> High 'mid the clouds of Fame's bright sky
> Thy banner's blazoned folds now fly,
> And truth shall lift them higher.

On he went, through the last two stanzas. Not a cough was heard, not a chair scraped. No sound came until he finished, and then the thundering applause told him the audience had been moved by his protest, and they chose to

believe him instead of the doctor. Under cover of the
tumult, that gentleman was seen creeping out of the hall,
but nobody, least of all Paul, paid any attention.

He went on to present the program he had planned, full
of fun and charm: "The Rivals," "The Cornstalk Fiddle,"
"A Banjo Song," "October," and a number of others. Each
reading received a round of ringing applause, and afterward the people came crowding to the platform to congratulate Paul. "First rate"; "fine work"; "full of fire."
Phrases to remember when he was riding back on the train.

Some of them wanted to buy a copy of *Oak and Ivy*, so
he made several sales on the spot, and took orders for more
before he left to make the midnight train.

Mr. Thatcher was highly pleased. "You were a big success, my boy," he said as they drove back to the station;
very tactfully he made no reference to Dr. Chapman's remarks or Paul's effective reply. As they shook hands in
front of the depot he promised, "I'll write to you in a few
days."

Within the week Paul had a letter from him which contained an offer to finance a year at Harvard; he felt strongly
that Paul should have some college education. He wondered whether Paul could manage on fifty dollars a month;
if so, he himself would send a check for one month, and he
was certain he could find nine other men to do the same.
Members of the West End Club who heard Paul, and those
who bought his book were much impressed with his work
and had been talking it up. Interest in the young poet's
career was high. Perhaps they could arrange another appearance, more profitable than the first.

Before Paul had a chance to answer, a second letter, written on the same day, arrived from the lawyer's office. If
Paul would send an unpublished poem to the Toledo *Bee*,
the paper would print it, with a comment by the editor!

The Toledo *Blade* had also agreed to publicize Paul's work, and this would pave the way for his second engagement in Toledo. Mr. Thatcher had lost no time in promoting his career, and Paul was grateful to him.

However, when he thought over the offer of a college education, Paul decided that he did not want to take on the obligation. He would much rather pay his own way if he possibly could. He wrote as much to Mr. Thatcher, making it clear that he appreciated the lawyer's kind efforts. There was nothing Mr. Thatcher could do but accept the decision; but he did suggest that if Paul should happen to change his mind he shouldn't hesitate to write, and the loan would be arranged.

In a few days a copy of the Toledo *Bee* came in the mail; the "editorial comment" under Paul's piece said: "In Paul Dunbar, the young colored poet who recited before the West End Club, Ohio has a practical genius who will be heard from in the near future . . . He combines the ease and grace of a Riley with the sentiment and diction of a Longfellow." He added the clipping to his scrapbook proudly—he was in good company!

The Dayton *Herald* began to take notice of the increased publicity Paul was receiving. Although policy kept the editor from hiring him, there were roving-reporter assignments he could give him from time to time on a free-lance basis, and one of these came up a couple of days after Paul's Toledo trip. It was a feature story on springtime out at the grounds of the Soldiers' Home. Paul found a substitute to take over the elevator and went out to the Home with a photographer from the *Herald*. The story appeared in the Sunday issue, complete with photographs, decorations, and a "by-line" for Paul. Many *Herald* subscribers who had spent a leisurely Sunday reading the paper came by to tell Paul how much they had enjoyed the article.

If he could be sure of enough assignments like this one, as well as recitals, he thought, he would let the substitute take over his elevator job permanently.

For months everyone in Dayton had been talking about the World's Fair which was opening in Chicago during the month of May. Rob and "Leckie," who had gone to Chicago as they had planned and now had two little girls, wrote when preparations first began, suggesting that the whole family come to Chicago for the summer of the Fair. Lately they had been asking in every letter: "When will you be here?" Eugenie Griffin, who also had relatives there, was going to the Big City, she told Paul. "My aunt and uncle will introduce me to *the* Negro society!" she boasted. And although Paul laughed at her, he wondered if Rob could introduce him to big-city society—if he decided to go to the Fair.

He could not make up his mind. Chicago offered many opportunities, Rob said. Will and Meta had decided to go there for good this time—they had visited Rob, and found Chicago so much more exciting than a "hick" town like Dayton that they weren't satisfied with the West Side social life any more. Paul was perfectly satisfied with his friends, the parties, church socials and country dances, but he thought he might meet more literary people in Chicago —and he might find a better job, more suited to him. Still, the city was so huge, and, he felt, sinister in its intrigues and easy roads to vice; it scared him to think of going there to live, even for a summer.

Then one day the editor at the *Herald* sent word that Paul could do another feature story for the paper—"Dayton At the Fair"—if he went to Chicago. So he had a reason for going, just the incentive he needed. He gave notice to the Calahan building that he was quitting his job, and asked Ma if he could take the old suitcase Pa had left. "I'll send

it back so you can pack your things in it when you come,"
he said with a reassuring smile. She hadn't objected to his
trip, but he knew she dreaded the thought of being left
alone.

And he had a hard time leaving her, when the day came.
He was sorry, too, that he had to give up seeing the garden
at the new house come into bloom. The lilac buds were
beginning to unfold, and, if he and Ma counted right, the
snowball bush would be a white mound of blossoms in a
few weeks. They had never had a garden as nice as this
before—and it belonged to him. The thought that he
owned a house and lot, but in name only till the mortgage
was paid, made him more anxious than ever to win fame
and fortune.

The first two or three weeks in Chicago brought precious
little of either one. Boys from all over the country had
flocked to the city for the Fair, and they were all seeking
work. For every job there were a hundred applicants; the
Fair would not be open till the middle of May, but everyone wanted to be set with a job when the day came.

There was a place for Paul to sleep at his brother's, but
the family was cramped as it was in the small flat, and he
did not feel he should stay with them indefinitely, so he
made every effort to find work. He ended by taking a job
as a waiter in a downtown hotel.

The dining room was large and crowded with tables, to
handle as many customers as possible. An extra number of
waiters had been hired to take care of the expected increase
this summer; they were friendly fellows, who, like Paul,
had come to Chicago for the big event. In between rush
hours, they had time to stand around and talk, generally
about their girls; and they usually gathered near the swinging doors leading to the kitchen. The waiters who were
busy, passing through with loaded trays, would call out a

warning: "Jump back!" If nobody moved—and usually nobody did the first time—they would tease, "Jump back, honey, jump back!" Without halting their stories, the boys would jump; and in Paul's ears the repeated warning gave the gossip a syncopated beat that tickled him. One night he scribbled in his notebook:

> Seen my lady home las' night,
>   Jump back, honey, jump back.
> Hel' huh han' an' sque'z it tight,
>   Jump back, honey, jump back.
> Hyeahd huh sigh a little sigh,
> Seen a light gleam f'om huh eye,
> An' a smile go flittin' by—
>   Jump back, honey, jump back.

When he went off duty later, he hurried to his rooming house and added two more stanzas to the lines he had already set down. He called the poem, "A Negro Love Song."

Among his fellow waiters Paul found another who wrote poetry, James Carrothers, who was a "space" writer for Chicago newspapers, paid by the column for any stories that were accepted. He worked in the dining room during rush hours, since his free-lance earnings were far from steady, although the pay was $6 a column, he told Paul. Six dollars; that was higher than the *Herald* or any Dayton papers offered. It was worth a try, and Paul spent several evenings knocking out news stories with a human interest slant, which he hoped editors might buy.

Downtown Chicago, where he worked, was dark and dreary with its narrow streets a maze of soot-covered office buildings that shut out the sunlight; a pall of smoke from factories and stockyards seemed to hang over the business section even on the brightest days. And when the

wind blew its hot acrid breath across the city, tainted with
the stockyard stench, foul with factory dirt, Paul felt it
was like a blast from the bowels of the earth. He could
hardly bear to breathe until he was well out of the area
where incredible wealth piled up behind those dingy doors,
and sharp-shooting politicians bought and sold human welfare as if it were part of the meat-packing industry. He
found relief only when he reached the South Side, where
he had taken a room in a boarding house close to Rob and
Leckie's flat.

It was not too far from there out to White City, the
name that had been given to the Fair grounds because of
the gleaming alabaster buildings that were rising in a
splendor of whiteness on the shore of Lake Michigan.
They were close to completion, and nearly every night
curious crowds came out to see what progress had been
made. To Paul, after the nightmare of downtown Chicago,
it was like coming upon the Elysian fields. The classic
Greek architecture of the huge pavilions lent a stateliness
and purity to the scene, which stood out like a bas-relief
against the sky-blue waters of the lake. Paul gazed with
something like awe at the Court of Honor, at the marble-
like columns of the balustrades, the formal gardens with
splashing fountains, the gondolas gliding on the lagoons.
And when the electric lights were turned on, White City
changed into an enchanted city, right out of a fairy tale.
The whole place glowed and sparkled like an immense
jewel.

Benevolently floating above were the emblems of the
two countries that had made possible this Columbian Exposition, as the Fair was formally called, to celebrate the
four hundredth anniversary of the discovery of America—
the Stars and Stripes fluttered beside the red and gold of
Spain.

The great opening day arrived in the middle of May. President Cleveland was on hand to press the button at the proper moment, and the Fair began. Paul heard of a job as washroom caretaker at one of the main buildings; he would have liked something better, but he had come to Chicago for the Fair and he wanted to be part of it. He applied and was hired at once at a salary of $10.50 a week, more than he had earned at any job so far, and it was "a soft snap," he said in his letter to Ma telling her about it. (As soon as he was a little ahead he would send for her.) He worked from two in the afternoon until seven in the evening, only five hours, so he had plenty of time before and after work to see the sights, to roam from one exhibit to another taking in the wonders of science and invention. Of course there was a carnival side to the Fair—the carrousel, the Ferris wheel, the shooting galleries. And there were the representations of various countries—"Little Egypt"; the exotic "Turkish Village," dominated by a mosque; the exciting "Streets of Paris"; and best of all, Paul thought, the Japanese Gardens, with quaint pagodas and pointed bridges over winding streams and tiny waterfalls.

Once the Fair was opened, the whole city began to hum. Chicago itself was like a carnival. Holiday crowds poured in from all parts of the country; people rushed out to the Fair grounds early in the morning, and stayed till late at night, when the throngs were swelled by those who could not be there during the day. Some visitors who were not used to walking so much had to take to their beds for a day or so because they were running a temperature—"exhibition fever," it was called. Of all this, Paul wrote in detail for his "Dayton At the Fair" article, which he sent to the *Herald* soon after the exposition started.

Sometimes he lingered quite late at one exhibit or another, and one night it was eleven-thirty before he got back to his boarding house on Armour Avenue. When he came into the dimly lighted vestibule, he noticed a large package on the hall table—and it was addressed to him, from Ma! The oblong box was awfully light, he thought as he carried it to his room; what could be inside? Quickly he pulled off wrapping and lifted the lid. He saw a mass of soft whiteness on a bed of green leaves—blossoms from the snowball bush! There must be a riot of bloom in the front yard by now, and Ma knew how much he had wanted to see it. Leave it to her to think of sending him a sample! He put the bouquet in water, and sat right down to thank her. He assured her again that he would be sending for her very shortly, as soon as he could save enough out of his salary.

He began to make friends at the Fair. People had a way of striking up conversation during a time like this, and within a few days fast friendships were formed. One of the young men Paul met this way was Wendell Philips Dabney, music teacher and "world's champion guitar-player," he introduced himself with a grin. His guitar was strung around his neck on a silk cord, and he would strum a tune in the midst of his chatter. Through him Paul met another musician about their age—a violinist by the name of Joseph Douglass. He loved Joe's playing, but when the boy mentioned one day that his grandfather was in charge of the Haitian exhibit, Paul grew so excited he forgot the violin completely.

"Don't tell me you're Frederick Douglass's grandson!" He couldn't get over it. The great leader, famed orator and statesman, was a close relative of this new friend.

"That's right," Joe said smiling. "But I like to say he's *my* grandfather."

Paul laughed. "Either way, I guess you can both be

proud," he said. "I'd rather meet your grandfather than any commissioner here," he went on. "I've followed his work ever since I first read about him at Intermediate school. Do you suppose . . ." he began, then stopped abruptly. "Oh, but he probably never heard of me," he finished.

A day or so later Joe came running up to Paul and told him some remarkable news: his grandfather had read about Paul Laurence Dunbar in a Washington paper, and he had been keeping track of the young poet's work!

Joe had more to tell. "He says, if you could come up to his rooming house tomorrow, he would like to meet you."

"*Can* I?" Paul's eyes sparkled. "Man, just show me the way!"

After work the next night he didn't loiter at the Fair a minute, but hurried back to the boarding house and put on his best suit, which he had been saving for just such an occasion as this. He shined his shoes, and knotted his newest tie around the collar of a clean shirt. He was waiting impatiently when Joe came to call for him, and they took off for Mr. Williams', where Douglass was staying.

Mrs. Williams opened the door and invited them in, but she had some disappointing news. "Your grandfather just went to get his dinner, Joe," she said. "He thought you were coming earlier."

"Oh!" Paul could not keep from showing his feelings.

He was so crestfallen Mrs. Williams suggested that the boys might follow Mr. Douglass to Wheeler's boarding house, where he was in the habit of taking his meals. The boys rushed over, and waited in the boarding-house parlor.

Later that night, Paul described the meeting dramatically in a letter to Ma:

"The old man was just finishing dinner. He got up and came tottering into the room. 'And this is Paul Dunbar,' he said, shaking hands and patting me on the shoulder. 'Paul, how do you do? I've been knowing you for some time and you're one of my boys.'

"He said so much, Ma, that I must wait until I am with you before I tell you all. He had me read to him my 'Ode to Ethiopia' and he himself read to us with much spirit 'The Old Tunes,' with which he seemed delighted. I gave him a book although he insisted on buying it. 'Well,' he said, 'if you give me this I shall buy others.' So I expect to sell him two or three anyhow.

"I am in the very highest society Chicago affords. We went Sunday evening to call on Mrs. Jones, an old lady who owns a seven-story business block in the heart of Chicago. She is over seventy years old and worth over $200,000.

"After all her boasting, Eugenie Griffin is not in it. I am invited and arranging to attend a reception at this Mrs. Jones' house given to five distinguished Englishmen who want to see some of the representative colored people in this country. And think, Ma, your poor little ugly black boy has been chosen as one of the representative colored people after being in Chicago only five weeks.

"I forgot to say that Mr. Douglass invited me to visit him at his home in Washington next winter and stay a while. He said, 'It would do my heart good just to have you there and take care of you. I have got one fiddler (his son) and now I want a poet. It would do me good to have you up there in my old study just working away on your poetry.' "

Paul ended his letter by asking Ma to box up the rest of his books and "express" them to him right away; he had the feeling that he would be selling a good many copies soon. He had received an invitation to recite his poetry with Jennie O'Neill Potter, a young reader who recited with Riley, at an "aristocratic hall" in the city. People there might well buy copies of *Oak and Ivy*. As he sat staring out of the open window at the midnight stars above Armour Avenue, he could almost see the hand of Providence held out to him.

The next week he was able to send for Ma. She came bringing with her an atmosphere of home; she had wanted to cart her chickens along, too, but Paul convinced her there was no place for a "few laying hens" even in outlying South Chicago. He found a room for her in the building where Rob lived with his family, so she could run in to see her grandchildren any time.

He did not have much time to be with her himself after the first few days, when he escorted her through White City (watching her eyes widen at the wonder of it all). When he was not at his job, he was writing some piece of poetry or prose, hoping to help out his income. One day he took a little poem down to Mr. Charles Dennis, the editor of The Chicago *News-Record*, who had written to Paul several times when he accepted a manuscript. He was undecided about taking the present poem; he would have preferred another one of Paul's dialect pieces, like those they had published some months ago. "Not everyone can write dialect poetry," he said. "You have a real gift for it."

That night at the Fair, Paul talked the question of dialect poetry over with Jim Carrothers and some of the others who gathered in the coffee house at the Haitian exhibit. There was quite a group of them—Wendell Dabney and Joe, with several singers and musicians; two composers, Harry Burleigh, who taught at the New York Conservatory of Music, and Will Marion Cook, who had been a classmate of Dabney's at Oberlin. Jim Carrothers had brought along a poet friend, James Campbell, also from

Ohio. He admitted he had tried to turn out dialect poems, but none of them had been published.

"I don't know what the trouble was," he said. "They just didn't seem to have any appeal for the editors."

Jim Carrothers said he had never even tried. "The medium is too difficult for me."

Too difficult! Paul thought. For him it was easy as pie.

He would have liked to hear more, but Will Cook wanted them all to "get down to business" on his pet project. He had been trying to promote a Colored Americans Day at the Fair. The plan was opposed by a good many Negroes, who were afraid that false newspaper publicity would picture the affair as a watermelon feast or a cakewalk jamboree. Not that there was anything wrong with either one, but cartoons and minstrel shows had given white people the impression that Negroes were not capable of enjoying a higher, more thoughtful sort of entertainment. Even Douglass was dubious about the success of Will's plan, and so far had refused his consent.

"Why don't we ask him to be the main speaker?" Wendell asked.

"Dabney, you're a genius!" Will clapped him on the shoulder.

The boys went in a body to the Williams', where they found the old orator poring over a copy of the Constitution, which he often studied. He listened to their request patiently, pleased that they were asking him to head the program, but still doubtful. He finally gave in, on the condition that there would be no distasteful publicity. The boys assured him they would not let any facetious stories get into the papers; they would even print circulars saying, "No watermelons, no Negro jubilee," to be handed out at the Fair on the day of the celebration.

As Paul was about to leave with the others, Douglass

asked him to wait; and when they were alone, the leader told him he had made a place for Paul in the Haiti office. "I can't offer you more than five dollars a week," he apologized. He would have to pay Paul's salary out of his own pocket, as there were no funds for extra help.

Paul hardly stopped to consider the fact that he would be earning only half as much as he did now—just to be close to the celebrated leader, working with him, was enough.

He started as assistant in the Haiti exhibit the following week. Now he was truly a part of the Fair. He met, or sometimes interviewed important personages who came to see Frederick Douglass, or to look over the exhibits in the pavilion. One of those who came to study the agricultural display, showing the processing of sugar cane, coffee beans and other Haitian products, was George Washington Carver, a young artist and science student at Iowa College. His painting, "Yucca Glorioso," hung in the Art Palace as part of the Iowa State exhibit, but he was more interested in odd, scientific facts about horticulture than anything else.

During his off hours, Paul had more social engagements than he could keep. At the reception for the Englishmen, he met a young school teacher from Washington, D.C.—Rebekah Baldwin—who introduced him to a circle of active intellectuals, working in the Capitol for the betterment of life not only for Negroes but for all people. One of the women, Mary Church Terrill, had already made a name for herself as a "suffragette." At parties, these recent college graduates sat up till all hours talking hopefully, spiritedly, of the future, until even Douglass, discouraged as he often was, took heart again.

"A new Heaven is dawning upon us," he said; "a new earth is ours in which all discrimination against men and

women on account of color and sex is passing away and
will pass away."

The days spun busily by. Paul was happy as a lark at
his new post, and like the lark he sang, through his poetry.
Will Cook had commissioned him to write an ode for
Colored Americans Day, and he had begun on it at once.
Sometimes at night the boys all went out to the races at
Washington Park, not far from the Fair grounds, to take
in the sights, if not the races. Paul kept his notebook
handy, and jotted down phrases or different kinds of speech
he heard; occasionally he spouted verses on the spot, to the
delight of his companions. About the middle of July, he
was able to attend some of the sessions of the Literary Congress, where he saw and heard the great Richard Watson
Gilder, editor of *Century*, the magazine Paul still put first
when he started a poem on its rounds.

August 16th was Haiti Day at the Fair, celebrated with
an informal reception, at which he was kept busy shaking
hands as he stood beside Mr. Douglass and Joe in the
reception line.

Nine days later, on Friday, August 25, a torrid heat wave
heralded Colored Americans Day, starting early in the
morning when Paul came to the office. The celebration
was scheduled for 2:30 in the afternoon, and he wondered
how many people would show up in the 100° temperature.
He was troubled, too, by the rows of watermelons that
fruit vendors had set out, expecting a big sale in spite of
the circulars the boys had distributed.

Frederick Douglass was heartsick at the sight. "You
see!" He flung an accusing look at Paul. "They're making
a farce out of it after all!" He jammed his Panama hat on
his head and went back home. "Take care of the office,"
he mumbled as he left.

So Paul sat at his desk all morning and answered questions. One reporter kept prying until he was ready to throw the man out. But he quietly stated that the sole celebration consisted of speakers and musical performances in Festival Hall at 2:30. The reporter left in a huff, determined to send in a story written for laughs. Without waiting for the program, he banged out his copy in time for the afternoon edition, "Few Colored Folks There; Negroes Apparently Not Interested."

As early as one-thirty, however, nearly three thousand people had formed in orderly groups, and stood waiting for admission. When the doors of Festival Hall opened, they trooped in quietly, a well-behaved crowd. The only parcel of clowns in the house was a group of teen-age boys in the gallery, who had come expecting to see a minstrel show. They waited impatiently while Frederick Douglass introduced the honorary vice presidents of the day, and the guest of honor, Mrs. Isabella Beecher Hooker, sister of Harriet Beecher Stowe. When Douglass began his address, "The Race Problem in America," reading it from typewritten pages, the hoodlums let out a hoot of disappointment—jeers and catcalls, plus a few hisses rained down upon the speaker.

For a few minutes, Douglass went right on reading his paper, beads of sweat glistening on his forehead. Then, as the racket in the gallery grew more raucous, he suddenly threw the typewritten pages on the podium, and fixed a fiery eye on the rowdies above. In a moment he had been transformed from an aging statesman, worn out from the strain of the past few weeks, to the fighting orator he had been as a young Abolitionist. Paul felt a thrill run down his spine as the old man, thrusting a hand through his lion's mane of white hair, roared out the mighty truths which came from his soul:

"There is no Negro problem. The problem is whether

American people have loyalty enough, honor enough, patriotism enough to live up to their own Constitution. We Negroes love our country. We fought for it. We ask only that we be treated as well as those who fought against it."

As the words rolled on, like the rhythmic call of the drum roll stirring the people to battle, the jarring notes from the gallery were stilled; the jeers were heard no more. And when, after almost an hour, he stopped speaking, a storm of applause poured from his enthralled listeners. He had to raise his hands, quieting them down so the program could continue.

There were several short speeches, followed by the musical portion of the entertainment, which included solos by J. Arthur Freman, Harry Burleigh and Sidney Woodward, as well as a duet from Will Cook's opera, *Uncle Tom's Cabin*. Joe Douglass played his violin.

Paul's poem came next. He stood up from his seat on the platform. "I will give you an ode," he said modestly, "written expressly for this occasion: *Colored Americans*." Down in front, where Ma was sitting, no one needed to ask who she was—her face plainly said, "That's my son!"

In spite of the hectic start, Colored Americans Day was a huge success, as the stories in the newspapers the next day showed. Paul and Ma pored over the pages for his "notices," delighted with every one they found. "Paul Dunbar read an original ode, *The Colored Americans*, which strode in stately meter," said the Chicago *Herald*. The *Record* reported that his poem received "a tumult of applause." And the *Tribune* referred to him as the author of *Oak and Ivy*, which was the kind of recognition he needed.

It brought him a number of reading engagements, and still more reviews. Frederick Douglass told more than one person that he thought Paul was "one of the most promising young men of our time"; he gave a copy of his book to Paul, with the inscription: "From Frederick Douglass to his dear young poet friend Paul Dunbar, one of the sweetest songsters his race has produced and a man of whom I hope great things."

Although a severe depression was spreading over the country, the Fair lasted until October 28. There was talk of holding it over till the next year, but when the Mayor of Chicago, Carter Harrison, was murdered by an office-seeker who had been disappointed, a shocked city felt it would be unfitting to continue the celebration.

After the exposition closed, unemployment hit Chicago as well as other cities. Paul decided to go back to Dayton to look for a job, but Ma was going to stay on at Rob's for a while. She would be a help to Leckie, who had been ill. Rob was hard up, but he wanted her to stay, too, so Paul kissed her good-bye and took the coach to Dayton by himself.

It had been a glorious summer, he thought as he watched the scenery fly by outside the train windows. A little like being on a perpetual merry-go-round, but that had only made it more fun. Far from winning any fortune, he had less now than when he had gone to Chicago in June—he had even pawned his watch before he left so he could loan Rob the money—but he felt much richer. He had gained something more precious than gold.

CHAPTER XIV

Gloom Follows Glare

THE FIRST thing Paul saw when he came down Main Street was a long line of people outside an empty store; it was a "soup kitchen," the notice on the corner told him. People had been laid off at National Cash Register and other large firms by the hundreds; every day the lines grew longer, the people grew hungrier.

Paul was grateful for his old elevator job at the Calahan building, which he was able to get back only because the man who had it left town unexpectedly.

Once more the familiar routine began: "Fifth floor, please."

"Yes, sir." (*What rhymes with mignonette?*)

163

"Third floor, please."

"Yes, ma'am." (Met? Let? Set? Wish Ezra would come in.)

He gave recitals around town with some of the boys from Philodramian, and also some of the girls who had helped in those productions. One of the programs combined music and readings; his cousin Dora and Mabel Finley played piano solos, Randy-Tams read several comic pieces, and "Paul Dunbar gave four original recitations."

One advantage of the elevator post was that he could easily arrange for out-of-town readings. He went to Richmond for the fifth time, called back "by popular demand"; to Xenia; Yellow Springs; and Springfield. If this kept up, he would be on a regular "circuit" like a vaudeville actor!

The trips kept him from being too lonely, in the house by himself while Ma stayed in Chicago. Sometimes Bud or Randy spent the night with him—Charley had married Julia Galloway, one of Paul's former girls—but most of the time he was alone, and he found that the house seemed bare without Ma. One night he cooked a big fat hen for Bud and himself, but it didn't seem to have any flavor—or maybe it was because he didn't have much appetite. The next day he started a poem called "Lonesome," and the second stanza said:

> We've killed the fattest chicken an' we've cooked her
>   to a turn;
> We've made the richest gravy, but I jest don't give
>   a durn
> Fer nothin' 'at I drink ere eat, er nothin' 'at I see.
> The food ain't got the pleasant taste it used to have
>   to me.
> They's somepin' stickin' in my throat ez tight ez
>   hardened glue,
> Sence mother's gone a-visitin' to spend a month er two.

The fourth went on—

The neighbors ain't so fren'ly ez it seems they'd ort
    to be;
They seem to be a-lookin' kinder sideways like at me,
A-kinder feared they'd tech me off ez ef I wuz a
    match,
An' all because 'at mother's gone an' I'm a-keepin'
    batch!
I'm shore I don't do nothin' worse'n what I used to do
'Fore mother went a-visitin' to spend a month er two.

There were plenty of girls in Dayton who would have
been more than happy to keep Paul from being lonesome,
or "keepin' batch." He was more in demand for parties
since he came back than he had ever been, and he usually
accepted all invitations promptly. He was a favorite with
out-of-town girls, too, who came to visit their Dayton relatives. He wrote them letters when they went back home,
and occasionally he enclosed a poem. One of these was
too good for a "mash-note," he decided, so he sent it to
Munsey's, a national magazine, instead. And the editor
bought it—his first sale to a national magazine!
However, he was far from being of a mind to marry, and
at times he wished he were not quite so popular, especially
when one girl, Maud Clark, took to stopping in at the Calahan building almost every night, just when he got off work.
This meant that he usually walked her home, and occasionally her mother asked him to stay for supper. In a
town like Dayton, if you were seen walking home with a
girl two or three times in succession, you were practically
engaged to her. And Paul had no intention of becoming
engaged to any girl until he had come a lot closer to his
goal—or at least, until he fell in love; and so far he had not.
He heard from some of the friends he had made at the

Fair. Rebekah Baldwin wrote from Washington that she was all wrapped up in her teaching again, and she wondered if he had found work. A letter came from James Campbell, too, telling Paul that he was principal of the West Virginia Colored Institute at Farmville. He liked the work, but he wished he could be as successful as Paul in having a book published. Paul smiled, reading James' words. He wondered which was better—to be published, and take in an occasional dollar as he did from *Oak and Ivy*, or to earn a steady income from teaching and not have to worry. It was really a toss-up, he decided.

He kept on with the readings whenever the chance arose. One of the engagements took him to Louisville, where Ma had lived so long ago; he saw for himself the "ol' Kentucky sights" he had seen through Ma's eyes—the fields of blue grass, waving in the wind; the white mansions on the hilltops; and the weatherbeaten Negro shanties below. He met his Uncle John, Ma's brother, and heard enough plantation talk to furnish him with material for a dozen new dialect poems.

He began to receive inquiries about his recitals from various clubs and organizations that were interested in having him come to read, and one day after work he went to see Orville about getting a folder printed, which would give all the facts of his career and set him up as a "pro." Orville was glad to take on the job—work in the shop was slack because of the depression, so he could get the folders out right away.

"We'll make it a classy job," he said, hauling down some heavy glossy sheets. "How's this?"

Paul thought it would do very well, and they decided to use blue ink. A picture of Paul, taken for the Western Writers' Association, would fill up the front cover; below it, the caption announced:

"Paul Laurence Dunbar, The Negro Reader
140 West Ziegler Street, Dayton, Ohio"

Page 2 of the folder was devoted to "The Old Tunes,"
and the third and fourth pages contained seventeen testi-
monials to Paul's talents as both reader and writer.

Orville had the order ready in a week, and when Paul
came to pick up the packet of folders he said, "You just
got in under the wire; another few weeks, and someone
else would have to do your printing."

Paul was used to the way Orville spoke in riddles, but
this one puzzled him so he couldn't even guess what his
friend was talking about; Orville finally told him in confidence that he and Wilbur had decided to give up the
printing business and open a bicycle repair shop. Both of
them were mechanically inclined, both liked to "monkey
around" with machinery, to try out new ideas. Bicycles
were all the rage now that the new safety bike with wheels
of the same size had come out in place of the old "high-
wheelers" that were so hard to balance.

"Even the ladies can ride the new bikes," Orville said,
his blue eyes laughing, "So we're expecting to do a rushing
business in repairs."

Paul laughed, too, and told Orville some of the comments
he had been hearing from older ladies who rode the elevator to the dressmaker's on the fourth floor. "It seems
there's a new *divided skirt*," he mimicked the shocked tones
of one of his passengers, "for girls who ride, and old Mrs.
Grundy said, 'I'd rather see my daughter dead and in her
grave than riding to hell in one of those things!' "

Orville hooted, and Paul picked up his package and left,
humming *A Bicycle Built for Two*. He was sorry the
Wright brothers were giving up the print shop, but he had
an idea they would do just as well with the repair shop;

Orville, he knew, could put wings to any notion that came into his head.

The new folders were "classy" and even impressive, Paul thought, but they did little to increase the number of requests he received for recitals. The gloom of depression cast a shadow over the entertainment world too.

He was having trouble in keeping up the payments on the house. Ma's laundry work had not brought in much, but it had been enough to let them make ends meet. Paul's salary by itself would not stretch that far, and when the recital fees fizzled time and again, he began to fear he would lose the house altogether. Ma wanted to come home, but he couldn't send her the fare, and Rob had no money to spare. In September Bud went away to medical school at Western Reserve in Cleveland at long last; Paul was happy for his friend, but lonelier than ever after he left.

Rebekah Baldwin wrote from Washington that there was a place open for an English teacher in her high school; if Paul would apply, and find some prominent person to vouch for him, she thought he would stand a good chance of receiving the appointment. He sent in an application at once, and appealed to Dr. Alexander Crummell, a well-known Washington minister he had met at the Fair, to speak in his behalf. The clergyman did what he could, but Paul was not appointed because he was not a college graduate.

It was a vicious circle: he couldn't get a better job because he didn't have a college education, and he didn't have the money to pay for the education! "It's almost funny," he said to Ezra, who stopped in at the Calahan building the day Paul received word of his turn-down.

To add to his troubles, another recital was canceled at the last minute, without any advance notice, and this organization had promised by letter to pay him twenty-five dollars. The cancellation was a real blow. There must be some way of collecting the fee. He decided to ask Mr. Thatcher in Toledo for advice. The lawyer, as usual answered Paul's letter by return mail; since the organization had offered the fee in writing, their letter was the same as a contract, and would have to be made good. Paul could certainly collect.

Kind-hearted Mr. Thatcher! When Paul wrote to thank him for his interest and advice, he couldn't help asking whether the funds offered for college the year before were still within reach; he needed some money now—not for further education, but for a place to live. If he didn't make the mortgage payment, he would lose the house. He was terribly worried.

In a few days, Mr. Thatcher sent fifty dollars, enough to cover all of Paul's expenses and send for Ma besides. Paul lost no time in putting her railroad fare in the mail.

Ma was home. Life was suddenly easy again, breezy again. The cornpone was hot when he came home from the Calahan building, and at night the ghosts were gone from the stairs. Full of new-found zest, he wrote a packet of poems and shipped them off to *Century;* and he sent a few to other magazines, too. *Blue and Grey* accepted one called "The Two Brothers," for fall publication.

Then one day in December, when the first snow was flying and the bells of cutters tinkled above the powdered pavements, Paul found a marvellously thin-looking envelope from *Century* lying on the parlor table when he came home. Scarcely able to breathe, he tore open the flap, and pulled out a letter from the assistant editor, R. U. Johnson, with these magic words:

"We are inclined to accept the contributions you are good enough to offer us for 'In Lighter Vein.' Give us a reference, as you are a stranger to us; e.g., my cousin, Mr. C. U. Raymond, will vouch for you if you know him."

He went shouting into the kitchen, waving the letter. "Ma! Ma!" In his exuberance a pun popped from his lips: "The turn of the *Century!*" He grabbed her and did heel-and-toe with her, round and round the kitchen table; he was a good dancer, light on his feet, but Ma could not keep up. She finally freed herself, puffing.

"Paul, you do beat all. Now, what're you hollerin' 'bout?"

When he calmed down, he told her. After all these years, they had at last accepted his poems. He sat down before supper to compose a letter to Mr. Johnson, and included as vouchers those from James Whitcomb Riley and Dr. Matthews. Mr. Johnson then came up with a real voucher from Thomas J. Wood, Brigadier Major-General, U.S. Army, who sent Paul a carbon copy of the letter for his files.

On December 17, Mr. Johnson sent back Paul's voucher letters and enclosed a check for three poems: "A Negro Love Song"; "Curtain"; and "The Dilettante." The first would be published early in the new year; "A Negro Love Song" would appear in the April issue. Paul thought of the boys waiting on table in the Chicago hotel and smiled. He never dreamed that the little poem in dialect would be the first published in *Century*. He felt that it must be a sign, and he saw, as if he were looking through an open door into the future, a whole flood of dialect poems in print surrounding his name, which was in enormous letters. But he was probably getting way ahead of himself. "Jump back, honey, jump back," he laughed softly.

CHAPTER XV

Bursts of Light

H E FELT like singing all the time since *Century* had accepted his work. New poems began filling the pages of his tablet in the elevator; stories, too, took shape from his winged spirits, and manuscripts from Ziegler Street went zooming out across the country to every likely magazine or newspaper. The name of Paul Dunbar was growing more and more familiar to editors. And the stack of clippings for his scrapbook was also growing. Published pieces appeared in the New York *Times, Munsey's, The Chicago Magazine, Blue and Grey,* the *Independent.* Not all of the publications paid, but most of them did, or they offered a year's subscription in exchange for a manuscript. And Paul discovered with delight what all writers quickly learn: that one acceptance leads to another. In fact, once the ice was broken with the first, *requests* for more manuscripts flowed in. The *Independent*, which had printed several of his poems, turned down "Retrospection," but asked if he had any stories on hand. He sent in "Anner Lizer's Stumblin' Block," a hilarious tale Ma had told him about a young belle's "salvation" in the plantation church, and the editor snapped it up for the May issue.

When the story came out, a columnist on one of the Dayton papers happened to read it, and remarked in his paragraphs, "Paul Dunbar is one of the young men Dayton is proud of."

Mrs. Conover showed him the line when she stepped into the elevator that day; he had not seen the paper. "I expect you know that I've been proud of you for a long time," she said.

Paul smiled happily. "Thank you for believing in me, Mrs. Conover." He could say it, now that he was beginning to see his name in high places. He showed her the copy of *Century* he had just received, containing his poem, "Curtain." It was a few lines of pure fun, which he had scribbled one night after he and Randy had seen a melodrama put on by a traveling theatrical troupe:

> Villain shows his indiscretion,
> Villain's partner makes confession.
> Juvenile, with golden tresses,
> Finds her pa and dons long dresses.
> Scapegrace comes home money-laden,
> Hero comforts tearful maiden,
> Soubrette marries loyal chappie,
> Villain skips, and all are happy.

It was a great thrill, Paul told Mrs. Conover, to hold in his hand issues of the revered *Century* which contained *his* work along with that of all the most respected writers. All during the months that he sat in the elevator, studying and poring over a copy of *Century*, he never really believed he would make it, but he was grateful to her for encouraging him.

The next week end he went to Cleveland for a recital, and he took both April and May issues along to show Bud. His friend had a great deal to tell him in turn about medical school, and the two sat up half the night, talking, "catching up." Before going back to Dayton, Paul went to Toledo, where Mr. Thatcher had invited him to speak a second time at the West End Club. It was a most successful evening, especially as the lawyer saw to it that there were copies of *Oak and Ivy* for sale after the meeting. He was doing everything he could to help Paul's career. When he came to Dayton on business, he brought more orders for the book. Everyone at the Club had been taken with Paul's humor and charm, he said. People hoped he would write more poems like those new ones he had read from *Century*.

But not all the poems Paul wrote that spring were humorous. On February 20, Frederick Douglass had died suddenly, a few hours after delivering one of his fiery speeches. The old warrior had died with his armor on, and the whole Negro race felt the loss of their leader. Paul mourned him further as a friend, someone he had turned to for strength and comfort, a man who was mighty, yet wise and understanding. A young poet's deepest feelings went into the memorial ode Paul wrote for the services on April 7, held to pay tribute to a great spirit. He titled it simply, "Frederick Douglass," and as he read the opening of the ninth stanza, his voice trembled with emotion:

We weep for him, but we have touched his hand,
And felt the magic of his presence nigh . . .

During the same month, a famous novelist spoke in Dayton—George W. Cable, who wrote Creole stories and had just published an antislavery historical romance, *Grandissimes*. Paul saved his money for a seat in the gallery; he didn't want to miss such an important colleague, one who had done so much for justice for Negroes. In the morning on the day of the lecture, Mrs. Conover came into the elevator earlier than usual, looking a little excited. Paul happened to mention that he could hardly wait till evening, he was so anxious to hear Mr. Cable; he wondered if Mrs. Conover would be there. She was not only going to hear the novelist, but she was entertaining him that afternoon at tea, she told Paul. No wonder she seemed rushed to keep her appointment at the dressmaker's!

Later, just as Paul was going off the job, he saw a small boy come running across the lobby, waving an envelope in his hand.

"Mr. Dunbar, Mr. Dunbar!" he was calling. "Note from Mrs. Conover."

Paul quickly opened the envelope. Inside was a note inviting him to meet Mr. Cable backstage after the program! He hurried home, bolted down the pork chops Ma had prepared, and left her bewildered as he dashed upstairs to shine himself up for the evening.

He was in his seat ahead of time, peering down over the gallery railing to get as good a view of the speaker as he could. George Cable was a distinguished-looking man, slim, black-bearded, elegantly careless as he came onstage with a book tucked under his arm, and another in his hand, his finger holding open one of the pages. When he sat down in the speaker's chair, Paul's eyes almost popped out of his head—the book in Cable's hand was not his novel, but *Oak and Ivy!* Paul knew that small, brown volume couldn't be anything else. The historical romance, from which the author was going to read, had evidently been shoved aside while he pored over Paul's poems. Only after he had been introduced, did he pull it from under his arm.

Then the program was over, and Paul was backstage before the applause had died away. In a moment Mrs. Conover had introduced him, and he was shaking hands with George Cable. He thought the meeting would end there—people were beginning to collect in a little crowd around the speaker, asking for his autograph—but the famous author told him to wait, and afterward they "talked shop" for over an hour, while Mrs. Conover and her sister, Miss Mary Reeve, stood listening. Like a pair of literary cronies, the two writers compared notes on rhymes and metrical rules, on critics and critical reviews, on the queer quirks of editors and the audacity of some authors in asking for fabulous terms. They turned to social reform, and the question of education. Paul was amazed to learn that such a widely read novelist as George W. Cable had never been to college, nor had as much formal education as Paul. Orphaned at the age of fourteen, he had to go to work, but had studied literature and history by himself in the early hours of the morning; he used to get up at four o'clock, he said, so he could put in a couple of hours before he went on the job. His story was both a comfort and an inspiration to Paul. The conversation ended with an exchange of compliments; Mr. Cable had many words of praise for Paul's poems, particularly those in dialect, and Paul had no trouble finding words of admiration for the older writer.

As Paul walked slowly home in the soft starlit night, he seemed to reflect its quiet glow. Happy, yet thoughtful, he determined to work harder than ever.

May was as beguiling as a young girl that year, and Paul was fancy free. He had just broken off a half-hearted engagement to Maud Clark, who had been pestering him to marry her, and now he promptly fell in love—with a photograph. One evening after supper, as he was leafing through the Boston *Monthly Review*, he noticed beside one poem the arresting face of its author, Alice Ruth Moore. It was an unusual face, not beautiful in the accepted sense, but full of intelligence and charm. The eyes were enormous, the nose was pert and saucy, the lips were small and shapely. In fact, the whole picture was so appealing, Paul kept turning back to it again and again. Furthermore, the poem was very good; here, at last he saw a girl who seemed to be not only sweet and pretty, but bright and witty—he must become acquainted with her.

For some time he had been carrying on literary correspondence with a number of Negro writers whose poems he had come across in various magazines. Why shouldn't he write to the lovely Miss Moore as well? Just to express his admiration of her poetry, of course . . . He composed a reasonably formal letter that night. He mailed the letter before he went to bed; and as he dropped the envelope in the box, he figured how long it should take for an answer —two days to get to New Orleans, where Miss Moore was teaching; two more for the return—well, allowing her one day to write, it shouldn't be more than five until he heard from her.

But five, and even ten days passed, and he did not hear from Miss Alice Ruth Moore. In the meantime, he accepted a temporary job as editor of a Negro newspaper in Indianapolis, the *World*. He would only be filling in while the regular editor was away on vacation, but the position, even temporarily, was another step in the direction he wanted to go. He loved the work, and threw himself into it with such ardor, that he almost forgot about the letter to New Orleans. Then one day when he came from the *World* office to his boarding house, he found the reply from the girl whose picture had prompted him to write; and her opening sentence, explaining the delay, sounded exactly the way he would have expected her to be:

Dear Sir:
> Your letter was handed to me at a singularly inopportune moment—the house was on fire.

He could have hugged her! But he had to find out what happened . . .

> So I laid it down, [the letter read] not knowing what it was, and I must confess, not caring very much.
> After the house was declared safe and the excitement had somewhat subsided, I found it laid in my desk and read it somewheres about ten days later. . . . I was not to blame, being partially blind and suffering from a bad hand burned in the fire. But I enjoyed it nevertheless when I did read it, and those dainty little verses have been ringing in my head ever since I read them.
> I must thank you ever so much and though I don't like to appear greedy, still if you have any more like them, please send them down this way. Your name is quite familiar to me from seeing your poems in different papers. I always enjoyed them very much. You do a great deal of work in different lines which is fortunate for you since you have the entree in so many of our best papers.

She went on to discuss some of the questions he had asked, and she spoke of her own career, mentioning a little volume of short stories which she had "in press" just then; she supposed he would take a copy. She closed by saying, "I shall be pleased to hear from you soon and often." To Paul "soon" meant immediately, so he sat right down and wrote an answer, boldly asking Alice to send him a picture of herself. She might also submit some "contribution" to

his paper, he suggested, a story or poem; he knew he would
be sure of hearing from her quickly—no writer could resist
a request for "material."

About the middle of June, when the roses smiled on
every fence, Ma sent Paul a big boxful of them from their
yard, along with a reminder that the payment was due on
the house. He went home for his birthday on the twenty-
seventh, and found the check in payment for "Anner
Lizer's Stumblin' Block," but most of it went to the building and loan company, and to the Wright brothers, for the
printing bill he still owed on the folders. There wasn't
much left for a birthday celebration, but he and Ma had a
good visit. Instead of giving a party, Paul wrote a poem
about one—a real shindy Ma had told him about long before. He read it aloud to her when he finished. Judging
from Ma's chuckles, it was one of his best dialogue pieces.
When he described how one smart-aleck guest,

> Kep' on blund'rin' 'roun' an' foolin' 'twell he giv' one
>   gread big jump,
> Broke de line, an lit head fo'most in de fiahplace right
>   plump;

Ma had a regular fit of laughing, and Paul himself could
hardly go on:

> Y'ought to seen dat man a-scramblin' f'om de ashes
>   and de grime.
> Did it bu'n him! Sich a question, why he didn't give
>   it time;
> Tho'ow'd dem ashes and dem cindahs evah which-a-
>   way I guess,
> An' you nevah did, I reckon, clap yo' eyes on sich a
>   mess;
> Fo' he sholy made a picter an' a funny one to boot,
> Wif' his clothes all full o' ashes an' his face all full o'
>   soot.

Well, it almost stopped the party, the poem went on, except that right then the hostess, Mandy, "happened on de spot/ To invite us out to suppah," and the way Paul told about that supper was so realistic that Ma, like the listener in the poem, was practically falling on the floor. "Eggpone jes' like gol'; hog jole, bilin' hot, an' steamin' roasted shoat, an' ham sliced cold; chittlin's," and "gread big sweet pertatoes, layin' by de possum's side." And at the preacher's blessing with

> One eye shet, an' one eye open, dis is evah wud he
>   said:
> "Lawd, look down in tender mussy on sich generous
>   hea'ts ez dese;
> Make us truly thankful, amen. Pass dat possum, ef you
>   please!"

Ma let out an approving, "Mm-mph! That's a fact, Paul—the bigger the feast, the shorter the blessin' every time!"

The poem ended with a lively scene when they cleared the cabin "fu' to dance dat suppah down." The fiddler "chuned his fiddle," and "made it ring."

> Jigs, cotillions, reels an' breakdowns, cordrills an' a
>   waltz er two;
> Bless yo' soul, dat music winged 'em an' dem people
>   lak to flew.

They danced that way till dawn—"evahthing was rich an' prime"—Ma joined in the last line:

> An' dey ain't no use in talkin' we jes' had one scrump-
>   tious time!

As she wiped her streaming eyes, Paul suspected that a few tears mingled with her laughter, which was the effect he hoped his dialect poetry would have on all who read it. But for Ma, he knew, this poem had the special quality of remembrance, and so her pleasure had been doubly great. They both agreed that "The Party" they had just relived was one of the most successful they ever held on Ziegler Street.

Back at his editing job, Paul received his second letter from Alice. She had lost no time in sending a manuscript! This was a legend she had learned from the natives about old New Orleans, and Paul was glad she had been so prompt, because his editorship would be over soon, and the regular man might not have the same interest in Miss Moore's work that Paul did. She had sent her picture, too, and he set it on his desk, so he could look at her lovely face whenever he liked.

In July, the job was over, so he went home, unemployed for the time being; his place in the Calahan building had been filled, and there were no vacancies expected. At least he had plenty of time to write. He turned out several new poems, and mailed them to *Century*. He sent old manuscripts to new publications, to those he hadn't tried before. But the income from writing varied—one week you might sell something, but for the next three or four and sometimes more, nothing was accepted; or maybe the publisher was one who could not afford payment. It was a rewarding, yet discouraging profession, but he felt the rewards were greater than the disappointments and hardships, and he would not give up now that he was beginning to make some headway in the long climb to success.

He would be perfectly content if only he had a little more money to "manage" with!

The Western Writers' Association was holding a conference in Indiana, and Paul was scheduled to speak on short-story writing, using a story of his own, "The Luck of Lazy Lang," to illustrate his points. However, he was too short of funds to buy a train ticket, and there was no prospect of getting any. On the Saturday before the meeting, which was on Monday, he still had no money for his fare. He didn't like to borrow, but he wanted terribly to attend the conference, so he spent all day Saturday and Sunday going from one friend to another—Randy, Ezra, Charley—not one of them could spare the few dollars he needed, although he could see they hated to turn him down. He didn't want to ask Orville or Wilbur Wright; they had already loaned him too much by doing his printing jobs on credit. His relatives—Uncle Rob, Aunt Elizabeth, and Cousin Dora—wished with all their hearts that they could help him out, but they, too, had to say no. By Sunday night he was still as far from getting to Indiana as if he had been at the South Pole.

He went to bed, but he couldn't sleep. He kept thinking about the speech he was supposed to deliver at the meeting the next day. He had not written it because he had been too busy trying to borrow the money to go, but now points kept occurring to him. He finally got up about eleven-thirty, turned on the gas light above his desk, and started to write; near two o'clock, he finished the speech and threw down his pen. Somehow he felt much better, although he had no idea how he could possibly attend the conference. He went back to bed and fell asleep just as the town clock struck four.

Three hours later he wakened at his regular rising time, and got up. Something made him step outside for the morning mail before breakfast. He found a letter postmarked "Toledo," but not from Mr. Thatcher. It was signed H. A. Tobey, M.D., and as Paul started to open the pages, a check for five dollars fell out! That would cover his train fare and more! A special Providence must be looking out for him.

He scanned the letter quickly. Some friend of this Dr. Tobey (Mrs. Conover, Paul later learned) had sent him a copy of *Oak and Ivy*, and the check was to cover an order for five more copies; the doctor had been deeply impressed with the quality of the poems, so much so that he wanted to help the poet. The letter went on, "I have talked with a number of friends of mine and believe I am in a position to give you financial aid if you desire to increase your education or to travel with a view of better qualifying yourself to pour out your poetical songs to the world.

"When I was in Dayton I learned that your ambition is to become a lawyer. The world is already too full of lawyers for its good, peace, or welfare. What we need is more persons to interpret Nature and Nature's God. I believe you are especially endowed for this work. . . . I am anxious to assist or help you any way I can . . . write me and tell me what your ambition is and what you desire to do.

> Very truly yours,
> H. A. Tobey"

It was an unusual letter, one that showed sympathy and understanding, but Paul couldn't answer it properly at the moment. He had just time to get the books off, and catch the morning train for Indianapolis.

As soon as the conference was over, he wrote a long letter of appreciation to the doctor, dramatically telling the story of the way the check had saved the day. And then he came to the most important part, explaining his ambition to the doctor, and in doing so, he clarified it for himself, too. "I did once want to be a lawyer," he wrote, "but that ambition has long since died out before the all-absorbing desire to be a worthy singer of the songs of God and Nature. To be able to interpret my own people through song and story, and to prove to the many that after all we are more human than African." In those last words, "we are *more human than African,*" Paul had stated for all time his feeling about his people and his work.

A few days later, the mail brought more good news. It was beginning to be a pleasure to open the mail box these days! This was exciting—Will Cook, who had organized Colored Americans Day at the Fair, had set "A Negro Love Song" to music, and sold it to Witmark, the New York music publisher, he wrote. Here was a copy of the published sheet music for "Jump Back, Honey," as he called the song, and the contract from Witmark. What was more, he had arranged for this to be part of a musical called, *Clorindy, the Origin of the Cakewalk,* and could Paul write some more lyrics soon? "Sich a question!" Paul thought to himself; they were as good as done right then.

He did the cakewalk into the kitchen, waving the music. "My song, Ma!" he sang out. He tried to hum the tune and explain to her what it was at the same time. He was so excited he couldn't hit a note. He had to find somebody to play the music for him right away—Mabel Finley or Cousin Dora.

"Can't wait a minute, Ma—got to see how it sounds!" He rushed out, leaving her still not quite sure what he had been waving at her. She shook her head, grinning good-naturedly, and went on with her packing. She had just heard from Rob that Leckie and the baby were both sick, and Ethel had been severely burned when her clothes caught fire. He had sent railroad fare, and asked if Ma would come to "help out" for a bit.

Nearly every week a letter came from Alice; she and Paul were carrying on a real correspondence, and with each exchange of letters the feeling between them grew warmer. Paul broke out with a rash of love poems, and longed for a way to get to New Orleans. He dreamed about Alice, talked about Alice, and wrote about Alice—even to Rebekah, who wrote in return, "Please stop telling me about that Alice Ruth Moore!" and underlined it.

However, after Ma had left for Chicago it was Alice's letters that kept him from being so lonely, and so the mail delivery was the most important moment of the day. Sometimes of course he still received rejections—not printed slips any more, but letters. Mr. Johnson turned down the poems written just after the job on the *World* was over, and one of them, Paul thought, was rather good. It was a dialect poem which he called "When Malindy Sings," and in it he had described Ma's golden-toned voice, and the way it swelled the sound till you could hear it for miles around when she opened up her throat and let it go. The poem ended with the first line from "Swing Low, Sweet Chariot," and Paul had decided he would sing those words if he performed the piece on one of his programs. He was disappointed because Mr. Johnson had not taken it for *Century*, but he still liked the swing of it. He might even include "When Malindy Sings" in his next recital—whenever that might be.

It was sooner than he expected. Dr. Tobey wrote early in August, inviting him to give a recital for the mental patients at the State Hospital outside of Toledo, where he was superintendent.

Paul found a carriage waiting for him at the station in Toledo, and he enjoyed the five-mile drive along the Maumee River to the spacious hospital grounds, but he wondered whether he would feel strange performing in such an institution for the first time. He needn't have worried, however. Dr. Tobey had thoughtfully invited Charles Cottrill, a young Negro lawyer whom Paul had met through Mr. Thatcher, to be there when Paul arrived, and so he felt much more at ease than he had expected. And when Cottrill introduced him, the doctor's brusque kindness made him feel at home right away.

"Awfully glad you could make it," he said shaking Paul's hand vigorously. He had sharp blue eyes and a sharply pointed nose above a bristling brown mustache. "Don't you want to take your jacket off? This heat is stinking!"

Paul laughed and made himself comfortable. The reading proved to be much the same as many others he had given; the patients were both attentive and appreciative, awarding him with applause after every number. "When Malindy Sings" was highly successful; he even had to repeat the last stanza. From now on he would include it in his programs. Afterward, Dr. Tobey persuaded him to stay on a few days; he could use the library, enjoy the hospital grounds, which included a fishing pond, and in the evenings they could talk. The doctor's hospitable wife added her own invitation, and their three little girls— Louise, Helen, and Alice—joined in, too. They had loved the readings, especially "The Party" which Paul had also presented for the first time.

He found the hospital a most interesting place to visit. The 1,500 patients were free to roam the grounds; if they liked they could work in the flower or vegetable gardens, or help out in the barn and the dairy, for the doctor believed in a normal life as far as possible for those who were mentally ill. The green lawns and shrubs, the shady walks and retreats with benches every little way were part of his plan to help the patients feel happy.

Paul took walks, talked with some of the patients, went fishing with the little girls, and spent long hours reading in the library. At night there was much good talk. Samuel

"Golden Rule" Jones, the Mayor of Toledo; and Brand Whitlock, lawyer, writer, and future U.S. Ambassador to Belgium, were two of the doctor's closest friends. The three men were intellectual cronies, and liked to argue and chew over a subject the way Paul and Ezra did. They took Paul into the circle as a matter of course, and although at first he felt shy about being included, he soon entered into the discussions as heatedly as any of them.

He stayed in Toledo five days, and just before he left, Dr. Tobey offered him four or five hundred dollars for tuition so he could spend a year at Harvard, studying, reading, becoming a more educated writer. A year at Harvard—all he had to do was to accept the good doctor's gift, and his old dream would come true. But somehow he couldn't do it without thinking the matter over very carefully first.

Back in Dayton, he wrote to Ma about it, to Alice, and to Bud Burns. He thought about it a great deal; he had only a month to decide, and he saw little chance of getting the extra money he would need for clothes and books before school opened. Then, too, the payments on the house had to be kept up, so Ma would have a place to live. She couldn't stay at Rob's indefinitely, and Will couldn't keep her either. Furthermore, Paul still felt that he was the one who should take care of her since she had worked so hard in order to see him graduate from high school. In the end he decided to turn down the doctor's offer. He would go on as he had been, giving recitals, writing, earning his own way.

However, Dr. Tobey was bound and determined to help Paul by some means or other. He called on Mr. Thatcher, and the two benefactors put their heads together. They came up with the idea of sponsoring a second volume of Paul's poetry, only this time the guarantee was a gift, not a

loan. The books would belong to Paul, and the profits from
sales would all be his. As Paul read their letter, a wave of
warm feeling surged over him, and it seemed to him that all
good things must come from Toledo. A new book of his
poems was better than a year in College! Slightly giddy,
he caught the first train up for a consultation with the
team of Tobey and Thatcher: "T. 'n T., a powerful combination," he joked to himself happily.

Dr. Tobey had already consulted Hadley and Hadley,
a Toledo printing firm, and now they made the final arrangements for publication. The size of the book, the
number of poems, type size, "stock" or paper—all had to
be decided upon quickly because they wanted to get the
book out before Christmas, and it was already the third
week in October. Paul hustled back to Dayton to compile
his manuscript from the poems he had written since *Oak
and Ivy* was published three years before; if he had time,
he would compose some brand new ones, too.

He would include only a few, the best of those published
in *Oak and Ivy*, as he was quick to point out to subscribers when he started taking orders for the new volume.
He had no use for poets who brought out the same old stuff
year after year, disguised by a different title and a fancy
binding, with perhaps a few new pieces added for the sake
of appearances. He picked out eleven poems from *Oak
and Ivy*, and selected eighty-six from the later ones, which
added up to ninety-seven for his second book, nearly twice
the number in his first.

Next he had to decide on a title. He liked the idea of
the strong and the weak in *Oak and Ivy;* he would carry
it over now. He called the new book *Majors and Minors*,
placing the twenty-six dialect poems he had chosen at the
end, under a separate heading, "Humor and Dialect." He
still thought of them as "minor," although they were always

more popular at the readings than the others. He included the latest audience favorite, "When Malindy Sings," never dreaming that it would become one of his most widely quoted and long-remembered poems, set to music and sung by Negro and white alike.

The book did not come out till after Christmas, early in January 1896, but it was dated 1895 because the publishers were so hopeful of bringing it out before—just the opposite of *Oak and Ivy*'s appearance! However, Paul was happy to see a second book of his in print, whatever the date. The volume was neat and attractive, bound in green buckram, with Paul's picture under a tissue facing, inside, opposite the front cover.

Majors and Minors, like *Oak and Ivy*, was dedicated to Ma. He sent one of the first copies to her in Chicago so the whole family there could see it, and he inscribed it with a special verse to little Ethel, who was still recovering from the burns she had received.

Dr. Tobey was more excited than Paul over the publication; he was so impatient to see the poems in print that he got the first unbound copy off the press and slit open the pages with his pocketknife. "First-rate, superb!" he murmured to himself as he read, though he had seen most of the poems before.

He suggested that Paul come to Toledo to sell the book since he knew a great many people who would want a copy, and they could introduce Paul to others who would place orders for one or more. Paul was not as optimistic as the doctor, but he jumped at the suggestion. He had dreaded the idea of going around Dayton again, trying to peddle his poems. Nearly everybody he knew had a copy of *Oak and Ivy*, and although he assured them that *Majors and Minors* contained almost all new poems, he knew it was going to be difficult to make sales outside of the subscrip-

tions he had taken before publication. And for all the
confidence he had in his work himself, he still felt shy
about knocking on office doors, trying to get attention,
"tooting his own trumpet," as he told the doctor.

In Toledo, Dr. Tobey turned over the "Patrons" list
from the hospital to Paul, and went around with him personally introducing him to influential men in the city, who
might be able to publicize the book. Sales were easy when
the doctor was along; he was so enthusiastic about Paul's
work he made the prospective customer eager to lay hands
on a copy. But the doctor could not be away from the
hospital for long, and when Paul had to go on by himself,
he came up against the same old situation. More often than
not he was turned away at the front office, before he could
explain why he had come.

After a few days he was discouraged; this was worse than
applying for a job; he couldn't make another call—it was
too disheartening. He took the trolley back to the hospital
before noon and sought out Dr. Tobey in his study at the
end of the main floor corridor. Thowing the copies of
Majors and Minors on the desk, he burst out, "I swear I'll
never try to sell my own books again if I live to be a
hundred!"

The doctor smiled. "That's a long time, Paul," he said.
He tried to joke, but he knew what Paul was up against
and it was no laughing matter. "Why don't you memorize
a set sales talk?" he asked more seriously. "And let 'em
have it as soon as you come into an office."

Paul shook his head gloomily. "I wrote one out last
night and had it down pat this morning. Soon as somebody
glowers at me or gives me the cold shoulder I can't remember the first word."

The doctor rubbed his chin thoughtfully. After a moment he reached for his scratch pad and scribbled some

names on it. "Three friends of mine have promised to buy
your book, provided you bring it in yourself. They'll be
expecting you, so you won't have any difficulty at the door
—just give your name." He pulled off the top sheet and
put it in Paul's hand with a little pat. "Now let's see if
you can still smile."

Paul managed a pale grin. "Thanks, Dr. Tobey." He
left the study and started up the long hall toward the
center door. Halfway there, he heard the sound of small
feet running behind him, and turned around just as little
Louise Tobey caught up with him. Her golden curls
bobbed around her face and she was holding out to him
a white rose. "I brought it to you," she said breathlessly,
"from Papa's vase."

Now Paul smiled all over and suddenly felt he could
assail all the business offices in downtown Toledo. "Thank
you, fair lady!" He bowed low as he placed the rose in his
lapel, and Louise giggled delightedly, capering around him.

He made the three sales in no time, and even went on to
sell two more copies before he came back to the hospital.
When he did, he went right to his room and set down on
paper the lines of a poem that had been taking shape in his
mind all the way home. It was written in the style of a
seventeenth century ballad, and he titled it, "To Louise."
He read the lines aloud to the family the next morning:

> Oh, the poets may sing of their Lady Irenes,
> And may rave in their rhymes about wonderful
>   queens;
> But I throw my poetical wings to the breeze,
> And soar in a song to my Lady Louise.
> A sweet little maid, who is dearer, I ween,
> Than any fair duchess, or even a queen.
> When speaking of her, I can't plod in my prose.
> For she's the wee lassie who gave me a rose."

There were three more stanzas.

Little Louise sat on the edge of the sofa, looking proud as any princess, and Dr. Tobey declared that such a poem must be put in print right away. He sent it down to the Toledo *Blade* that very day.

The sale of the book spread. Dr. Tobey was the best private press agent Paul could have found. Nearly every day he brought someone home to meet the young poet, or sent Paul into town with a letter of introduction to some person of importance, heads of other hospitals, or of organizations that might ask Paul to read, and sell copies of his book after the recital. The untiring doctor even wrote to friends out-of-town, telling Paul's story; to Colonel Robert Ingersoll in Washington he sent a copy of *Majors and Minors* as well as a letter; he wanted to be sure the noted writer, lawyer and orator would read Paul's poems.

One night toward the end of April Dr. Tobey decided to stay in town after a late consultation, as he often did instead of driving way out to the hospital at that hour. He went to the Boody House, a busy hotel that catered to traveling men and theatrical troupes. Just as he was leaving the desk in the lobby he met an old friend of his, and they had hardly exchanged greetings before his hand went into his pocket to bring out a copy of *Majors and Minors*. "Paul Dunbar's new book," he said, and with only a word or two of explanation, he began to read. The friend, who at first had looked bored, grew more and more interested as the doctor went on; and the night clerk stopped sorting bills to listen, resting his chin on his hand, one elbow on the desk. A guest who came in for his keys stood still at the counter, forgetting to go to his room.

When the doctor finished, the listening guest introduced himself—Mr. Nixon, from the cast of *The Count of Monte*

Cristo, playing at the Auditorium. "That's a wonderful poem," he said. "Who wrote it?"

Dr. Tobey showed him the copy he was holding, and briefly told Paul's story. Then Mr. Nixon began to read in his rich, resonant voice, "The Poet and His Song." There was music in the lobby of the Boody House that midnight and much later, for the actor read on till the early hours, and the doctor was not one to stop him.

Mr. Nixon ended by buying the copy of *Majors and Minors* from Dr. Tobey, who described the whole scene to Paul the next day. Paul confessed that he had been listening to an actor, too, but it had nothing to do with business. James Herne, the famous playwright, was performing in his hit play, *Shore Acres*, and Paul could not resist spending fifty cents for a gallery seat.

"The show was worth every cent, though," he said. "You ought to go, Dr. Tobey! *Shore Acres* is a great play, and Mr. Herne is just as good an actor as he is a writer."

Dr. Tobey slapped his hand on the desk. "I've got an idea, Paul! The night clerk said Mr. Herne and the *Shore Acres* company were staying at the Boody House, too. I think you should take a copy of the book down there, and give it to Mr. Herne personally. If he takes a shine to it, you'll get ten times the cost of the book in publicity."

Paul thought the doctor's enthusiasm led him to exaggerate, but he followed the suggestion anyway. At the Boody House, however, Mr. Childs, the night clerk who had listened to Paul's poems, told him that Mr. Herne had moved to a quieter hotel, the Waldorf. When Paul inquired for the actor there, he received the cold stare and icy answer he had met with so often: "Mr. Herne is out." That was all. Rather than pursue the matter in such an unfriendly place, he went back to the Boody House.

Mr. Childs wanted to help; he felt as if he had a personal

interest in Paul since the other night. "I'm going right by there soon," he said. "I'll be glad to give your book to Mr. Herne."

Paul handed him the copy with a sigh of relief. But several days passed and there was no word from Mr. Herne. Paul wondered if the book had ever been delivered. Perhaps he should have seen to it "personally," as Dr. Tobey had said. He returned to Dayton the following week; he had been in Toledo nearly six months, and Ma was coming home from Chicago, and still had had no sign that the actor had received his book.

Then, a few days after he was back, a momentous letter came from Mr. Herne; *Shore Acres* had moved on to Detroit, so the actor had not been able to write immediately.

"While at Toledo a copy of your poems was left at my hotel by a Mr. Childs," Paul read. "I tried very hard to find Mr. Childs to learn more of you. Your poems are wonderful. I shall acquaint William Dean Howells and other literary people with them. . . ."

The rest of the letter was friendly, full of praise and good wishes, but Paul scarcely saw the words after he read that sentence. William Dean Howells—supreme literary critic, whose word was accepted as the top authority throughout the country! If Howells read his poems, and if he liked them—it was staggering to think about. The first "if" was greater than the second, so far as Paul was concerned. How could he be sure that Mr. Herne, famous, busy with the details and headaches of a play on tour, would remember to send a small volume of privately printed poems to the most revered critic in the land? Certainly he couldn't count on it, Paul decided.

In the meantime, Dr. Tobey had heard from Colonel Ingersoll, whose letter he sent on to Paul with a little note.

My dear Dr. Tobey:

At last I got the time to read the poems of Dunbar. Some of them are really wonderful—full of poetry and philosophy. I am astonished at their depth and subtlety. Dunbar is a thinker. "The Mystery" is a poem worthy of the greatest. It is absolutely true and proves that the author is a profound and thoughtful man. So the "Dirge" is very tender, dainty, intense, and beautiful. "Ere Sleep Comes Down to Soothe the Weary Eyes" is a wonderful poem: the fifth verse is perfect. So "He Had His Dream" is fine, and many others.

I have only time to say that Dunbar is a genius. Now I ask, what can be done for him? I would like to help.

Thanking you for the book, I remain,

Yours always,

R. G. Ingersoll

Dr. Tobey was elated over such a "splendid" letter from the Colonel, he said in his note; Paul should be greatly "encouraged."

And Paul was—but he didn't want to be carried away by hopes that might prove false. He had been hoping that Alice could come to Dayton on her way home to Boston after school closed in New Orleans, but her family would not hear of her stopping along the way. He wanted so much to meet her; each letter made him more sure of his love, and he had come right out with a poem called "Alice" in the new book; it was maddening to have to carry on a long-distance love affair. If she could not come there, he would see to it that he went East somehow during the summer. He set about lining up new recital engagements, and tried asking a higher fee wherever he could. (In Xenia, during the winter holidays, he had made fifty dollars in one night!)

He was out of town for readings through most of May and June. Coming back from one of the trips on his birthday, he found a hurried postcard from Dr. Tobey: "Get a copy of *Harper's Weekly* and read what William Dean Howells thinks of you."

Paul threw his briefcase on the kitchen table, gave Ma a peck on the cheek and practically ran all the way to the nearest newsstand. Out of breath, he tossed a dime on the counter. "*Harper's*, please."

"Sorry, we're all sold out."

Paul looked at him blankly, and the vendor explained that this was the convention issue, with the full story of Mc-Kinley's nomination by the Republican Party; everybody wanted to read it. After trying at several more stands, Paul finally got his hands on a copy and quickly flipped over the pages to William Dean Howells' section called "Life and Letters." With widening eyes, he read:

"There has come to me from the hand of a friend, very unofficially, a little book of verse, dateless, placeless, without a publisher, which has greatly interested me." Howells described the make-up of the volume; Paul's face, "with the race traits strangely accented"; and then he went on to discuss the poems and their author through the whole section!

"I do not remember any English-speaking Negro . . . who has till now done in verse," he ended the opening paragraphs, "work of at all the same moment as Paul Laurence Dunbar, the author of the volume I am speaking of."

The dialect poems reminded him of Robert Burns. "I do not think one can read his Negro pieces without feeling that they are of like impulse and inspiration with the work of Burns when he was most Burns, when he was most Scotch, when he was most peasant." He quoted two stanzas of "The Party," and spoke of "the jolly rush of its movement, its vivid picturesqueness, its broad characterization, and . . . the vistas into the simple, sensuous, joyous nature of his race Mr. Dunbar opens." Farther on, Mr. Howells quoted "When De Co'n Pone's Hot," and "When Malindy Sings," and commented: "I hope the reader likes as much as I the strong, full pulse of the music in all these things. Mr Dunbar's race is nothing if not lyrical, and he comes by his rhythm honestly. But what is better, what is finer, what is of larger import in his work is what is conscious and individual in it. He is, so far as I know, the first man of his color to study his race objectively, to analyze it to himself, and then to represent it in art as he felt it to be; to represent it humorously, yet tenderly, and above all so faithfully that we know the portrait to be undeniably like. . . . intellectually Dunbar makes a stronger claim for the Negro than any Negro has yet done."

The critic spoke of the "human" quality in the poems; he said they brought out the unity of all mankind, and that "perhaps the human unity . . . is to appear in the arts, and our hostilities and prejudices are to vanish in them." He mentioned the non-Negro dialect poems here—"Speakin' o' Christmas," "After a Visit," "Lonesome," and "The Spellin' Bee," all poems about Paul's "white neighbors" in Ohio, Indiana and Illinois. At the very end of the article, Mr. Howells noted the fact that this "significant little book" was printed by Hadley and Hadley in Toledo, his way of telling the readers where they could get a copy.

Paul felt as if he had been lifted into the high places with the light of heaven and earth shining upon him. He wanted to shout for joy, and at the same time a lump rose in his throat—a sound very like a sob came out when he started to ask the newsseller for another copy. Then, at the man's astonished look, he laughed.

"Never mind—I haven't got the dime, anyway!" He raced home, hugging *Harper's Weekly* to him all the way. Phrases from Mr. Howells' scholarly pen kept humming in his head. Most of all he cherished the part about "human unity": the great critic had caught the essence of those poems; he saw, as only a wise man could perceive, the aim that Paul was trying to accomplish.

"Ma, oh Ma!" He let the door bang behind him the way he used to when he came running home from school. "Just listen to this, Ma! It's by William Dean Howells, the highest authority in the land!" He read the whole thing aloud to her, from beginning to end, and the words rolled out and filled the kitchen like a hymn of praise.

"What do you say to that, Ma?" he demanded joyously when he finished.

"Hallelujah!" Ma said.

Dr. Tobey was jubilant as the young poet himself. With Mr. Thatcher, he planned a Fourth of July recital for Paul in Toledo, and invited Ma to come along. Mayor Jones and Brand Whitlock were on hand to congratulate Paul, and a large gathering of some fifty or sixty guests, including the Governor of Ohio, came to shake hands with him. Ma wanted to stay in her room, but Dr. Tobey said, "Nonsense! Who's more important than the poet's mother, I'd like to know? You must stand beside Paul, to help him receive the good wishes—I don't think he'll be able to hold up under the load by himself!"

The doctor was right. It was one thing for Paul to rejoice with his friends—or even mere acquaintances who stopped him on the street in Dayton after the article in *Harper's* appeared—and quite another to stand there in the doctor's hospital parlor, shaking hands, accepting compliments and praise from half a hundred people at once. Paul began to feel the strain of fresh smiles and a "thank you" every two minutes; he was so embarrassed it sounded silly to him after a while, and he wondered how long he could keep on. The doctor finally came to his rescue and carried him off to the study.

"Well, Paul," he said, "do you think you can bear so much acclaim in one dose?"

"I don't know," Paul smiled as he sank onto the tufted leather couch by the desk. "Right now I feel sort of numb!"

The doctor laughed. "Then I'm not worried. But I hope," he went on more seriously, "that you won't let this lightning recognition go to your head."

That night after dinner Paul was thoughtful and un-usually quiet. When he went to his room, he sat up for some time writing a poem, which he called "The Crisis." It was a prayer for divine strength in facing future "ap-plause," and he felt much better after the lines were down on paper. He gave a copy of the new poem to Dr. Tobey the next morning, and the doctor knew he need have no fear for the young poet he had sponsored.

"This means a great deal to me, Paul," he said. "I'll paste it in my scrapbook beside Mr. Howells' review."

Feeling light-hearted again, Paul went fishing with little Louise all afternoon; and in the evening they watched the Fourth of July fireworks set off by the city from the banks of the river. The display ended with a huge set piece—Old Glory itself, the stars and stripes streaming against the sky in a shower of light. Everybody clapped and cheered, but Paul's hurrahs had a meaning all their own.

CHAPTER XVI

A Place in the Sun

MA AND PAUL went home the next day. Paul opened the front gate for Ma and followed her in, but halfway up the walk they both stopped and stared at the shutters on the front windows, which were bulging with a white mass of papers like a stuffed wastebasket. Paul ran up and opened the slats, and out poured a rain of letters two hundred of them!

They were addressed to Mr. Paul Dunbar, from readers who had seen the piece in *Harper's*, and wanted to congratulate the poet. In thirty of them Ma and Paul found a dollar bill, advance payment for a copy of *Majors and Minors*.

"Land's sakes," Ma said, "You'll get writer's cramp if you answer all of 'em!"

But Paul, laughing, assured her he wouldn't feel any pain at all. There was one letter, however, which he had to write before he answered any of these, and that was to Mr. Howells. He had put off thanking the critic until he calmed down enough to express his feelings. He wrote on July 13th:

"Dear Mr. Howells:

I have seen your article in *Harper's* and felt its effect. That I have not written you sooner is neither the result of willful neglect or lack of gratitude. It has taken time for me to recover from the shock of delightful surprise. My emotions have been too much for me. I could not thank you without 'gushing,' and I did not want to 'gush.'

Now from the depths of my heart I want to thank you. You yourself do not know what you have done for me. I feel much as a poor, insignificant, hopeless boy would feel to have himself knighted. . . .

The kindly praise that you have accorded me will be an incentive to more careful work. My greatest fear is that you have been more kind to me than just." He ended by mentioning that he had written to Mr. Herne also, thanking the actor for putting the book in Mr. Howells' hands.

More letters came in the next few weeks, some to Paul and some to Hadley and Hadley in Toledo; orders for the book kept up all during July. Things were happening so fast that Paul's head swam when he stopped to think about it. Joseph Cotter, the teacher-poet who had booked Paul's recital in Louisville, wrote: "Go at once to New York and capitalize on this. Mr. Watkins of the *Courier-Journal* has written to Mr. Howells for you. You must recite for Mr. Howells. Be sure to give him 'The Party,' 'An Ante-Bellum Sermon,' and 'Whistlin' Sam.' 'Whistlin' Sam' ought to get New England. I can sell two books if you'll send them."

Dr. Tobey and Mr. Thatcher had already started making arrangements for Paul to go to New York. They thought he should have a professional manager, and had contacted one Major James B. Pond, a smooth-talking, fast-working agent who had handled lecture tours for Mark Twain, Henry Ward Beecher and other well-known personalities. Mr. Dennis from the Chicago *Record*, Mr. Howells, Brand Whitlock and others wrote to him about Paul also, and the Major agreed to take the young poet on as his client. He would make the living arrangements also. Dr. Tobey furnished the railroad fare, Mr. Thatcher a new suit, and before the end of July Paul found himself in the Big City. New York!

A month or two before he had been wondering how he would ever get to New York, and here he was, almost without having to lift a finger. The first thing he did was to let Alice know he was there—she could easily come in from Boston for a week end. He waited impatiently for her answer while he went around to publishers' offices with Major Pond.

The manager felt that Paul must have a regular publisher who would look after producing, selling and distributing his books. They called on Harper's as the most likely publisher; next they tried Appleton, and then Dodd, Mead. All three houses were interested, and they were equally good. Major Pond said Paul would just have to wait to see which one made the best offer.

Paul, waiting to hear from Alice, too, could hardly contain himself in the little boarding-house room the Major had rented for him. He walked among the crowds that

seemed to be forever rushing along New York's streets
(which were worse than Chicago in that respect), glimpsing
as best he could the "sights" of the town. The Flat Iron
Building, the Metropolitan Museum, Times Square, and
Central Park, and Madison Square, surrounded by fine
homes, where each household boasted its own carriage and
horses, and ladies drove out on sunny afternoons to take a
ride up through Central Park.

Alice wrote that she couldn't come to New York—her
parents refused to allow her to meet Paul—some brash
young fellow, they said, who struck up an acquaintance
with a girl through the mail, and then proceeded to send her
love letters. The idea! Of course Alice didn't agree with
them, but what could she do? She told him not to give
up hope, however; maybe she would find a way yet. Paul
was angry and disappointed, but cheered by the last part of
the letter. If Alice was trying to find a way to come to
New York in spite of her parents' disapproval she must
love him.

Mr. Thatcher happened to pass through New York on
his way to Narragansett Pier for a vacation, and asked
Paul to come there for a reading he would arrange at the
Matthewson Hotel. When Paul came into the ballroom of
the big resort hotel a week or so later, he sensed an atmosphere of festive excitement. Potted palms decorated
the dais where a string orchestra was beginning to tune
up; and a large company of guests, seated on elegant gold
ballroom chairs, greeted him with faces that spoke friendly
expectancy. He could feel it, strong as an electric current,
and something in him leaped to meet it. Like a professional
trouper, he stepped out to give his best.

As he read, he could see his listeners respond to "the
strong full pulse of the music" in his poems. Heads were
bobbing with the meter, and now and then you could hear

feet tapping to the rhythm on the polished ballroom floor. As he started "The Cornstalk Fiddle," he got "itchin' heels" himself, and suddenly, at the opening of the fifth stanza, he was dancing the steps as he called them off, while the orchestra struck up the square-dance tune in muted tones:

> "Salute your partners," comes the call,
>   "All join hands and circle round."
> "Grand train back," and "Balance all,"
>   Footsteps lightly spurn the ground.
> "Take your lady and balance down the middle"
>   To the merry strains of the cornstalk fiddle.

In the audience so many feet were keeping time Paul thought the people were going to spring up and join him any minute!

Almost before he finished there was a storm of applause, and after the program people came crowding to the dais to shake Paul's hand. Many bought copies of his book. He went to rest in Mr. Thatcher's room when the excitement was over, but he had just stretched out on the sofa when a porter came bringing a note from the widow of Jefferson Davis. She had heard the recital and enjoyed it so much she wondered if Paul would come to her room to give a private reading of a few of the poems for her!

"Too bad old Aunt Becca Porter can't see me," Paul chuckled as he straightened his tie and smoothed his hair. "Wait till I tell Ma!"

Mr. Thatcher was tickled, too. "I tell you, my boy, you'll be as famous in the South as in the North!" he exclaimed.

Paul was gone about an hour, and had been back only a few minutes when the porter rapped again, this time bringing a telegram from Major Pond. He had just signed a contract with Dodd, Mead!

They had made the best offer for the new book—$400 advance against royalties of 15 percent on the first 10,000 copies, and 17½ percent on all sales beyond that. Paul felt dizzy as he read the figures. It had been a fantastic day, and he was tired, but he had to write all the news to Ma, who was staying with Rob in Chicago again; she had rented the house in Dayton for seven dollars a month. Now at last Paul could prove to her that there was "big money in literature," and some of it was coming his way.

Paul's first book by a real publisher instead of a printer was to be a combination of the others, with an addition of nine new poems, written since *Majors and Minors,* two of which had appeared in *Century.* The editors at Dodd, Mead suggested the title, *Lyrics of Lowly Life,* for this volume, and Paul thought it was a fitting one. He dedicated the book simply, "To My Mother," without any flowery statements. William Dean Howells agreed to write an introduction; in it, he enlarged on the views he had expressed in his article, and added a few facts about Paul's life. It was quoted many times, and was used in 1913 as the introduction in the volume *The Complete Poems of Paul Laurence Dunbar.*

The production man at Dodd, Mead said it would be three or four months till *Lyrics* came out; in the meantime, Paul had a new picture taken, and breathed a sigh of relief at not having to worry about selling the book himself. No more tramping from door to door, trying to peddle his wares, suffering icy stares. He would bask in the sunlight of an established reputation, a reputable publisher. Aaaahh!

There seemed to be no end to this summer of thrills. Paul was invited to have dinner with the entire staff of *Century* magazine; he had to pinch himself as he sat at the big table and looked round at the faces who for so long had been legendary names—Richard Watson Gilder himself, and

R. U. Johnson, the poetry editor who had accepted "A Negro Love Song," and others whose names Paul used to look for when he held the fresh issue of *Century* in his hands every month, perched on the elevator stool in the Calahan building. Now they were men, making after-dinner speeches, using everyday gestures, like Mr. Gilder, smoothing down his walrus mustache before he began. Paul was called on, too. He decided to give them a few poems, one of them the popular "When Malindy Sings"; as always, he chanted the last line, "Swing low, sweet chariot," and cheers mingled with the applause that pealed out. Some imp made Paul turn to Mr. Gilder who sat next to him—he couldn't resist remarking, "That's one *Century* turned down!" Mr. Gilder's walrus mustache drooped lower as his mouth dropped open, but in a moment he recovered. "We'll take it yet!" he declared.

"Too late," Paul informed him gleefully, and even Mr. Gilder had to join in the shout of laughter that went up.

In September Paul appeared at the Lyceum Theater, and the reviews in the New York *Sun* and other papers were all favorable. Major Pond was well pleased with his new "inexperienced" client, and wrote Dr. Tobey to say he would like to sign Paul up for at least two years. The doctor thought he should get some advice before deciding, so he wrote to Booker T. Washington, President of Tuskegee Institute, who had come to the forefront as a leader after Frederick Douglass died. He replied that he himself had refused more than once to sign up for a lecture tour—one could easily become spoiled that way; he had written a personal letter to Mr. Dunbar, congratulating him, and offering any service he could give.

However, Paul decided to continue with Major Pond. So far the manager had promoted his career satisfactorily. Stories appeared in the New York papers—the Sunday

Journal ran a full-page feature article, with Paul's picture
—and Pond was already talking about contacting an English
publisher for a British edition of Paul's book.

The best professional event of this eventful summer in
Paul's life was, to his way of thinking, an invitation to visit
William Dean Howells at his home at Far Rockaway
Beach. He and the Major drove out there one sparkling
September afternoon in a horse-and-buggy outfit rented
from a downtown livery stable. At Far Rockaway, the
houses had no numbers. There was a row of cottages lining the road along the beach; the Major drove slowly in
front of them, wondering which could be Howells'. They
passed before one with a low, white picket fence, much
like that at Paul's place on Ziegler Street.

"I'll ask here," he offered, jumping down.

Just as he opened the gate and started up the walk, a
ruddy-cheeked man with a shock of short white hair hurried out of the door and down the steps. It was Mr.
Howells, running to meet Paul with arms outstretched!

"This is Paul Dunbar! This is Paul Dunbar!" he cried,
taking hold of Paul and drawing him toward the house.
"Come in, come in—I'm so happy to see you and meet you
personally."

Paul had never expected to be greeted so warmly by the
great critic; he was smiling all over, inside and out, as Mr.
Howells led him up the steps. Soon the two were talking
like old friends about books and authors, and the technique
of writing itself. Mr. Howells gave Paul the same advice
Mr. Dennis had given him in Chicago: "Write more dialect
pieces—they're your contribution to American letters!"

On and on they talked; Mr. Howells insisted that Paul
and the Major stay for supper, and over the clam chowder
and cold chicken Paul learned that Howells had lived in
Dayton as a boy, when his father tried unsuccessfully to

make a go of the Dayton *Transcript*, which failed after a
short time. "I was born with printer's ink in my veins,"
Mr. Howells said smiling, "and that's a dangerous disease
—the lifelong itch to write."

It was ten in the evening before Paul and the Major
finally rose to leave Far Rockaway. As they stood on the
porch making their farewells, Mr. Howells noticed that

Paul was shivering in the cold night air, damp with the early autumn wind blowing in from the ocean. He went to fetch his own overcoat, which he put around Paul's shoulders, nor would he listen to any polite refusal. The next afternoon Paul drove out by himself to return the coat with his gratitude—he would have been very cold without it driving back the night before. "But of course I felt like the ass in the lion's skin," he said.

"Nonsense!" the critic laughed. "Come back soon."

Century accepted two new poems, "Protest," and "Parted," which Paul wrote one night when he was feeling moody because the Moores would not allow Alice to come to New York. It was terrible to have her so close and still out of reach. He and Alice were being "parted" even before they had met—it was so unfair! He wrote continuously when he was not making appearances, in order not to brood about the problem. He sent some of his work to the New York papers and saw it published in the most important ones—the *Tribune*, the *Journal*, the *World* and the *Sun*. He went out with his composer friends from Chicago days, Harry Burleigh and Will Marion Cook, and they introduced him to two talented brothers, James Weldon and J. Rosamond Johnson, who would become his good friends. He would have been perfectly happy if he could only have found a way to meet Alice.

When the chance to give a reading in Washington came along, he took it. He was glad to see Rebekah again, and Molly Terrill, Joseph Douglass, Hallie Q. Brown, and all the other friends he had made at the Fair. "This is divine," he told Ma in a letter. "I have a room in Mrs. Baker's lovely home, but take my meals out. Tomorrow I'm going with Joe to see the Widow Douglass. The trip here was fine. I did not have to take a Jim Crow car once, and the scenery through Virginia was beautiful."

Early the next month, *Lyrics of Lowly Life* came out. It was exciting to see his first professionally published book; the neat little olive-green volume with gilt-edged pages and gold lettering on the cover was somehow completely different from *Oak and Ivy*, or *Majors and Minors*. As Paul sat in the Dodd, Mead office, autographing a stack of "first edition" copies for the booksellers, he felt like an established author at last. And then to walk into a bookshop and see his book there, sometimes on display—oh, that was reward enough and more for his years of struggle!

The book sold very well, and received favorable reviews, in England as well as the United States. When Major Pond saw the British notices, he decided it would be a good idea for Paul to go to England himself and contact British publishers. The Major's daughter, Miss Edith Pond, was leaving in February for a trip abroad; she often worked with her father's clients, and could act as Paul's manager, arranging recitals, meetings with publishers, and supervise the voyage generally. The fast-talking manager mentioned an outrageous percentage of Paul's earnings that his daughter would receive for these services, but Paul could not resist the idea of going to England—he, Paul Dunbar, from Dayton, Ohio, in London, England, as a professional writer, and reader of his poems! He realized that the Ponds were going to make it hard for him, but he would try to keep his upper lip "well-starched," as he wrote to the doctor.

He went out to Chicago to say good-bye to Ma and the rest of the family—Will and Rob, his nieces and nephew. His Chicago friends had to give him a send-off, too; and the newspapers made the most of the fact that he was going to England. "Mr. Dunbar," one reporter wrote, "is a torch of hope to his race."

On the way back, Paul stopped in Toledo for a farewell visit with his friends there—the doctor and Mr. Thatcher, Brand Whitlock and "Golden Rule" Jones—who felt they had a share in Paul's career, as Paul assured them they did. He often called Toledo his "adopted home," and he marvelled especially at the unfailing goodness of Dr. Tobey and Mr. Thatcher. Before he left, Mr. Thatcher arranged two readings for him, both with a good-sized fee.

In New York once more, he had a dozen things to do before he sailed, and one of them was to write a farewell letter to Alice. Her parents had even forbidden her to come to New York for the big bon voyage party being given for Paul by Mrs. Victoria Earle Matthews, who had sent Alice a special invitation. The hostess told Paul she was planning a "grand affair"; Mr. Booker Washington and other notables would be there. As furious and disappointed as he was over Alice's forced refusal, Paul couldn't help looking forward to the party in his honor the night before his ship sailed. He dressed with extreme care that night, and his hands shook a little as he put the studs in the dress shirt the Major had told him to buy.

A great many people had already arrived when Paul entered the crowded drawing room, and made his way to his hostess. Mrs. Matthews had an odd little smile on her face as she accepted his greeting; she cast a hasty glance at the guests surrounding them, and motioned him to one side of the fireplace. In an excited undertone she murmured, "Alice is here!"

Paul could hardly believe his ears. "What? Where? Where is she?"

And then he saw her coming toward him from the other side of the room, threading her way among the guests; he moved to meet her, and they stood gazing at each other as if there were nobody else in the room. Except that she was prettier, Alice looked exactly like her picture, Paul thought; he saw the same sweetness in her face—and the mischief in her eyes.

"I ran away," she said simply, with a disarming little shrug of her shoulders. "I couldn't help it."

He could hardly keep from hugging her then, yet he did not even touch her hand. They stood in the midst of the chattering, laughing company, and had no need of words to tell them their love was alive.

In the next moment Mrs. Matthews came to claim Paul, and Alice was carried off by some young men who were trying to organize a "cakewalk" circle. After that he only caught a glimpse of her until toward the end of the party, when he managed to spirit her away from the others, and lead her to an alcove where a small, cane-backed loveseat stood screened by potted palms. Here they could talk by themselves, could say the things they had been wanting to say all evening. The first words Paul uttered popped from his lips when he sat down beside her and took her hand. Before he knew it, he had slipped a gold band—Ma's wedding ring—from the little finger of his right hand onto the fourth finger of Alice's left.

"Will you wait for me?" he asked, his voice husky.

"Of course," Alice answered. And so they became engaged.

His heart singing with gladness, Paul sailed for England in the morning. On the fifth day at sea, he sent word of his big news to Ma: "You will be surprised to hear that Alice Ruth Moore ran away from Boston to bid me good-bye. She took everybody by storm. . . . She is the brightest and sweetest little girl I have ever met, and I hope you will not think it silly, but Alice and I are engaged. You know that is what I have wanted for two years."

Looking through the porthole of the *S.S. Umbria*, he

caught "a glimpse of the moon like a half-closed eye" on
the gray mid-winter waves, and across them he could see
Alice's hand stretched out to him, the gold band circling
her finger like the light of the land. For a moment he
wished he could swing the bow of the ship around and
head back, but since he was a poet and not a magician, he
wrote a lyric to his love instead.

England at last—British soil, British scenery from the
train window, and finally, London fog! Paul's first taste
of the sprawling metropolis, shrouded in the yellowish-
green billows, was literally like a soft, damp sponge. He
described it like a Londoner: "If fog gets in your nose,
you sneeze; if it gets in your eyes, you weep; if it gets in
your mouth, you *swear*."

When the clouds cleared, and the pale English sun shone
on St. Paul's, London Tower, Trafalgar Square, and all the
rest, Paul still saw only flashes of the city as he went here
and there, socially and professionally meeting people under
Miss Pond's supervision. From publishers' offices to newspapers, to society drawing rooms they kept going continu-
ally, leaving him little time for sightseeing. He wrote to
Ma, "I am the most interviewed man in London," and if
it was not true in fact, it was in feeling. He hardly had a
minute to himself the first month or two, Miss Pond had
been such an efficient press agent. She had obtained so
much advance publicity that he was invited everywhere—
to tea with Henry M. Stanley, M.P.; to luncheon, to supper
after the theater. He could not get over the freedom from
prejudice he found in London drawing rooms. He was accepted as Paul Dunbar, the newly acclaimed American
poet, and the color of his skin mattered not.

He was invited to have dinner at the famed Savage Club,
whose members were highly civilized and accomplished
men—explorers, writers, actors, musicians, painters, sculp-

tors, and scientists. He had never been among so many distinguished men at once, and during dinner he did little but listen to the brilliant conversation; he almost forgot to touch his roast beef. As soon as the table was cleared, the head "savage" beat upon the board with his war club: "Brother Savages, you may smoke." His announcement was the signal for entertainment as well as cigars; songs, sketches, card tricks, even a sword dance. Paul knew he would be called upon, and decided to give them, "When Malindy Sings," with its choral ending. As he finished singing the last line, expecting to receive applause, he was astonished to find himself seized by four of the men, and lifted bodily to the center of the bare table!

"Wh . . . what . . . what have I done, gentlemen?" he sputtered.

"Blimey, you've made a bloomin' 'it, that's wot!" one of the actors shouted in cockney dialect, and the rafters in the old club dining room rang with laughter. One of the members explained to a still somewhat bewildered Paul that whenever a guest made a particularly fine contribution to the evening's entertainment, he was rewarded by the treatment Paul had just received.

Vastly relieved, and smiling broadly now, Paul thanked them for their strange tribute, and remarked slyly, "I'm glad you didn't put me *under* the table!"

Although he had dinner often in the best dining rooms, the rest of Paul's meals were meager enough. Miss Pond had provided him with a grimy attic room in a shabby London lodging house, and as he climbed the rickety stairs to his cubbyhole after leaving some elegant home, he had to smile at the irony of it; the night he came back from the Savage Club he was inspired to write a poem, full of prickling humor, "Within a London Garret High." He had little money to go on. Most of the profits from *Lyrics*

of Lowly Life had been used to pay debts on the house
and his expenses in New York. The recitals here did not
begin right away, and even though they were a success,
Miss Pond took so much of the proceeds he had only
enough left for a bare existence.

However, the recitals were an artistic success, the reviews
were good, and best of all, his book was to be brought out
in a British edition by Chapman and Hall, the same firm
that published *Oliver Twist* and *David Copperfield*.
Dickens and Dunbar, Paul smiled to himself proudly. If
he could schedule enough recitals, he might stay on indefinitely. He even wrote Ma and Alice to consider coming
to London, where they could live in freedom from prejudice.

Then suddenly even this small bubble of success burst
and vanished into thin air, pricked by sharp reality: the
London "season" was over. No more recitals, readings, or
entertainments could be counted on until fall, Miss Pond
informed him. She went off to Europe and left him flat.
She had no further responsibility for clients after the end
of the season.

Paul was completely flabbergasted—what next, he wondered. He tried to book recitals through an acquaintance,
but London was no longer interested. Queen Victoria was
planning to hold a grand Diamond Jubilee in celebration of
her seventy-fifth birthday, and the city was already agog
over the preparations.

He had hardly enough to pay for his garret room, and
would have been out on the street in a short time if he
hadn't run into Dr. Crummell and Hallie Q. Brown quite
by accident in the British Museum one day. They were
among a group who had come from Washington for the
Jubilee celebration; the minister was staying several months,
and as soon as he heard the trouble Paul was in because of

Miss Pond, he had the young poet move into the house he had taken for the summer. Here Paul could write, and stop worrying about recitals until the Jubilee was over.

For some time Paul had been thinking of trying his hand at a novel, and had already planned a story about a young man in Ohio whose parents wanted him to become a minister—just as Ma had wanted Paul to be a preacher. Although he had never said much to Ma, he had pondered a great deal over her wish during his last year at Central; and after he had decided to become a writer, there were times when he sat in the elevator at the Calahan building, bent over the blue-lined tablet scribbling "in the dark," when he wondered whether he had made the right choice. But he knew in his heart that he never could have been a preacher, and the hero of the novel expressed the same feeling—that he was *Uncalled*, the title Paul was going to give the book.

He wrote several hours each day, but now he took time to get a real look at the sights he had seen only in passing during the first weeks in London. He went to Westminster Abbey, and thought of all the famous poets enshrined there. He saw Gog and Magog in the Guildhall, and watched the Changing of the Guard at Buckingham Palace. He went to the theater—Covent Garden, and Drury Lane— with Dr. Crummell, and afterward to the celebrated inn, the Cheshire Cheese, where long ago Dr. Sam Johnson held court among his tavern friends. Like many tourists, Paul sat in the renowned doctor's chair, and was so tickled with the whole idea that he had to write a poem about it.

Toward the middle of May, Ambassador John Hay heard that Paul had been left stranded by his manager, and came to his rescue with an offer to arrange a performance under the auspices of the United States embassy. He took a special interest in Paul because of his own dialect pieces,

the *Pike County Ballads*, written in the rough and ready
jargon of frontiersmen. He introduced Paul to Samuel
Coleridge-Taylor, the composer-pianist, and suggested presenting them together in a joint recital. The composer's
father was a West African Negro, and he was eager to set
some of Paul's poems to music. He had written musical
settings for *Hiawatha*, but he had not tried songs or dialect
pieces. He chose nine of Paul's poems, and said they almost
sang themselves, before he put down a note.

The concert-recital was given on June 5, at the Salle
Erard, Grand Marlborough Street, and the program stated
that it was held "Under the immediate patronage of His
Excellency, John Hay, United States Ambassador." Paul
presented three readings in between the performance of his
songs, and Samuel Coleridge-Taylor played his *Hiawatha*
sketches. The program printed both the titles and the
words of the nine poems, and Paul immediately mailed a
copy to Ma, and one to Dr. Tobey.

Following the recital, he received a flood of invitations,
like a real celebrity. Organizations like the Royal Society
of Painters and the Royal Geological Society asked him to
be the guest of honor at their meetings; he went to formal
teas and dinners in London homes, and spent enjoyable
week ends in country mansions. One elderly lady, Miss
Catherine Impey, to whom he later dedicated one of his
books, entertained him often, and made a point of asking
other guests who would give him publicity.

At most of these gatherings, he read his poems whenever
he was asked, and they were immensely popular. He was
wined and dined, sought after and praised—but he was not
paid; and while it was very pleasant to be a guest, he didn't
want to be a perpetual one. Furthermore, the reports sent
to the papers at home were embarrassing. One article had
him hobnobbing with royalty, "heir of a hundred earls."

Another release read: "Paul Dunbar, the Negro poet . . . is being lionized in London in most flattering fashion. . . . Being the latest literary novelty, he is much sought for receptions, garden parties, and similar gatherings. His readings of his own verses have been highly praised by the press, nor are the criticisms of the verses themselves less friendly."

Naturally, people at home thought he must be raking in a fortune; even Ma wondered why he couldn't send her a few extra dollars, although he had written to tell her what had happened. Actually, he didn't have tuppence to spare. He was not sorry he had come to England, and the past two months had made up for the hardships before; but he couldn't afford to stay on much longer, marking time till the new "season" began. He contacted Miss Pond about his return passage, and received the atrocious answer that she considered their contract broken because he had appeared under other sponsors; she did not have to furnish fare or ticket. She was taking the next boat home; Paul would have to find a way to get back by himself!

He was shocked and angry, but he couldn't waste time fuming. He had to borrow the money from somewhere; Dr. Tobey was the one person he felt he could turn to in such an emergency; he would understand, he would ask no questions. The money came from Toledo by return cable. Good, kind Dr. Tobey!

Paul packed up his clothes and the half-finished manuscript of *The Uncalled*, said good-bye to Dr. Crummell and his British friends, and sailed for New York.

All the way over he thought about Alice. He wanted to be married as soon as possible, but he wasn't sure he could support her on a writer's income. If he had a steady salary to rely on, he would feel much easier; he had sold four poems to the *Outlook* in May—"With the Lark"; "Time to

Tinker Roun' "; "Little Brown Baby"; and "When de Co'n
Pone's Hot"; and the demand for his work was growing,
but a married man needed more than a seesaw income.
Colonel Ingersoll had written that there was a possibility
of a job for Paul in Washington; perhaps it would soon be
a definite offer.

He found rather unexpected work when he reached New
York: his visit to England had surprising news value—all
the "yellow journals" wanted his views on Great Britain;
so, although he was disgusted with their desire for something sensational, he went into the "impression business,"
as he called it. Alice was still in Boston with her family;
he couldn't see her often, but he wanted to be nearby in
case she could get away for a week end. He spent most of
the summer writing "a Negro's impressions of England"
in the hot, sticky city.

In between articles, he worked on *The Uncalled*, and
Dodd, Mead accepted the novel, paying him an advance
on royalties. *Lippincott's Magazine* bought the serial rights,
and Paul felt in better "financial health" than he had for
many months. He sent Dr. Tobey most of the money he
had borrowed for his passage, and had enough left for Ma's
train fare back to Dayton. She had been wanting to go
home for some time; Paul wasn't sure when he would join
her—he didn't care to leave the east as long as Alice was
there.

Just as he was wondering what to do next, an invitation
came from one of his friends in Washington, Dr. Kelly
Miller, of Howard University: if Paul would like to come
to Washington, he could live at the Millers while he finished
his novel. Paul felt that he was indeed wealthy in terms of
friends! He took the first train for Washington, and
plunged into work.

The Millers made him feel at home right away; when he

wanted company, he could always join them, and when he was writing, they let him alone. There were times when he sat up till long after midnight finishing a chapter, and no one came near him except Mrs. Miller, bringing him a pot of tea to help him keep up his energy. On the other hand, if he felt like doing so, he could always relax in the living room with the family; and occasionally, in the afternoon, he played ball with small Kelly, Jr. (He gave the little boy one of the few copies of *Oak and Ivy* he had left, inscribed with a few rhyming lines of fun and affection:

> Dear Kelly, When I was a kid
> I wrote this book, that's what I did.
> When you grow up—I may be dead—
> You allus think o' what I said,
> Dat you gon' mek yo' ma'k fu' true,
> Cos, Kelly M.—I bets on you.)

Before many weeks had passed in the Millers' pleasant home and company, Paul was able to complete his manuscript and mail it to his publishers posthaste. He hardly had time to catch his breath when Will Marion Cook turned up in Washington with his brother John. "What about finishing *Clorindy* now?" Will wanted to know. It was high time, if they ever wanted to see the musical on Broadway.

Paul was tired from the push of completing his novel, but he thought the change of pace from a serious work to the syncopation of Cook's musical might be just what he needed.

The three of them went into action around a battered upright piano at John's house. Will hummed the tunes and John beat out the rhythms on the keys, while Paul paced back and forth composing the lyrics. As he spoke the words, Will jotted them down beneath the notes on his sheets of music, and soon a song was born. In some places, Paul was stuck for a rhyme, and Will would hand him a beer to help him over the hump. One by one, the songs took shape: "Darktown Is Out Tonight"; "The Hottest Coon in Dixie"; "Love in a Cottage Is Best"; "Dance Creole"; "Who Dat Say Chicken in Dis Crowd?" and the one which had been written first, "Jump Back, Honey."

Each song seemed better than the one before; the finished score, words and music, was alive with spirit, personality, sparkling humor.

"We've done it!" Will clapped Paul on the back and gave his shoulder a friendly punch. "You old genius, because of you, *Clorindy* is a hit, I can tell right now."

Paul waved him off, laughing, but Will said, "Wait till she gets on Broadway, you'll see," and hurried back to New York to start casting.

Only a few days before, Paul had received good news from Colonel Ingersoll—the Library of Congress had found a post for the young poet, starting at $720 a year. He headed for Dayton to sell the house on Ziegler Street as soon as *Clorindy* was completed.

He had intended staying only long enough to find a customer for the house and close the deal. "If you can pack up here," he said to Ma, "I'll go right back to Washington and pick out a nice place for us there." Ma agreed, but Dayton wouldn't hear of his leaving his home town without a proper send-off. He was their biggest claim to fame since he had been to England; stories of his adventures abroad had been blown up like the Arabian Nights tales. One of them was that he had taken tea with Queen Victoria at Buckingham Palace, and by the time Paul reached home it was so universally believed that he couldn't disclaim the honor. "I guess Queen Victoria won't mind if she finds out," he joked privately to Ezra, who nodded, laughing.

The boys from Philomathean were holding a reception for him, planned by Ezra as his closest friend in the club. All the Philo members from his class were on hand for the gathering—Bob LaRue, Ernest, Whyte, and of course Orville, and all the others. They stood in line and received the elders of the town who came to wish Paul well. Captain Stivers presented him with one of the hand-made violins Paul had watched him shape so lovingly; it was a gift to be treasured above many others. (Paul learned to play his cherished fiddle quite well, and wrote a poem to the comfort its music gave him.)

Later he inscribed a copy of *Lyrics of Lowly Life* for Ezra; "In memory of the days when you wanted to be a linguist and I a lawyer," and they both laughed, recalling their "two-man college" in the Calahan building.

"It's a good thing for you we didn't get very far," Ezra remarked, and Paul agreed.

Of course Mrs. Conover had to entertain for Paul. She invited her literary club to tea, and Paul was the guest of honor. At the last minute, standing beside Mrs. Conover to receive the members, he had a sudden sensation of shyness, the way he used to feel when he knocked on these ladies' doors, asking for odd jobs. "I've mowed their lawns, shoveled snow for them," he said under his breath to Mrs. Conover. "They know me as an errand boy."

"What of it?" countered Mrs. Conover. "If you can have tea with the Queen of England, you can have tea with the Dayton Ladies' Literary Club!"

Paul grinned. He was himself again when the first of the women came up to greet him, and Mrs. Conover said easily, "You remember Paul Dunbar, our gifted poet, who has just come back from England?" He bowed—the low, ceremonious bow Major Pond had taught him, and the ladies beamed, flattered and pleased. Some of them stopped for a

moment or two, reminiscing, congratulating him. But most
of them seemed to have forgotten that Paul ever was an
errand boy or an elevator boy. Now he was Paul Laurence
Dunbar, the famous poet, and they were happy to greet
him as a celebrity.

He chuckled, telling Ma about it afterward. "You'd
have thought they'd never seen me before. And I guess
maybe they never did," he added pensively. "Not really
. . ." His mood changed again as he came upon a stack of
old programs; he and Ma were going through the house,
weeding out the things they wanted to take to Washington.
"Oh, look at this, Ma—*The Stolen Calf!*—Philodramian's
first performance! I remember how scared we were that
night!" He decided to keep the dueling swords from those
days. "They'll be just the thing in case I have a study in
the new place," he said.

Ma had kept everything, old report cards, programs, the
copies of the *High School Times*, an old penknife and a
pair of rusty skates; and everything he picked up reminded
him of his "growing-up years." Before he went to bed he
wrote a letter to Bud, who was going into his final year in
medical school. "There are a heap of memories clustered
around this rickety old house," Paul confessed in the letter. He was surprised to find how much they had piled up,
and to realize that he would in many ways miss Dayton and
the life he had always known.

CHAPTER XVII

Success, Love, and a Parade

I N WASHINGTON Paul started house-hunting with a will
—and the help of his friends, especially the Millers and
Molly Terrell. If possible, he wanted to be settled by the
time his job began at the Library of Congress on October 1.
He wrote to Ma, telling her to finish the packing so she
would have everything ready to go when he sent for her.
A message to Alice carried the hopeful word, "Soon."
She was in Brooklyn now, teaching a huge class of sixty,
and felt that she should complete the year; they could be
married in June. But Paul hoped she would change her
mind once he had a home for her to move into; June was
too far away.

He scoured the neighborhood near the Millers, but hadn't
found what he wanted by October 1. His work at the

Library in the science stock room wasn't hard, but the
hours were long, and he had little time left for himself.
However, the people Paul worked with were friendly and
well-educated, and made him feel he was one of them.
There was a daily reading for the blind and before long
Paul was asked to take the hour with a program of his
poems. He was glad to oblige, and his listeners were more
than happy to have such lively entertainment instead of
the usual historical text or scholarly treatise.

At night he wrote short stories of Negro life. He had
had several published in magazines—the *Cosmopolitan*, the
Independent, Lippincott's; and Mr. Dodd suggested that
Paul try to turn out a few more, enough to make a book
of them, which Dodd, Mead would be glad to have on the
"spring list." It wasn't hard for Paul to find material for
a good many such stories in Washington. Thousands of Negroes who had headed north after the war had never gone
farther than the nation's capital; a whole community of them
lived in Howard Town outside the city, camped in rows of
shanties like those they had in plantation days. A new generation had grown up, but those of Ma's age and older
were ready to talk about old times to anybody who would
lend an ear, and Paul's was a willing one. Here were the
types Ma used to tell about—Aunt Doshies and Uncle Ikes
by the dozen—and Paul made the most of them. He would
jot down their speech in his notebook and out it would
come in one character or another when he sat down to
write in the evening.

One day in November Molly Terrell told Paul that the
people next door to them were moving, and he hurried to
take the house. It stood at the foot of the hill below
Howard University in a section called LeDroit Park. Paul
wanted to move in right away, and wrote happily to Ma:
"Come at once to 1943 Fourth Street, N.W. My house is

very beautiful and my parlor suite is swell . . . dark green plush and cherry-colored inlaid wood . . . polished floors . . . a study off the parlor . . . new bookcase . . . big fine Morris chair. The rent is $20 a month. I pay $22 now for board and room . . ."

The next thing was to persuade Alice that they should be married before school was out. As soon as Ma arrived to put the final "fixins" on the house Paul wanted Alice to come there. He had a good job, a fine home, and a steady flow of requests for his writing; all he needed was a wife, he argued.

But Alice's parents were still opposed to the match, and she didn't want to go against their wishes if she could help it; maybe she could bring them around, if he would just give her a little more time. However, when the holidays came and went without a change of heart on their part, Alice grew as impatient as Paul. Early in March she sent him a single-word telegram: "Come." He left on the first train. Her plan was that they could be married secretly so she could teach the rest of the year; then her parents could talk against Paul all they liked and it wouldn't matter; in June she would tell them she had been his wife for some time. She was like a staunch little general outlining her strategy, and Paul approved her scheme. Hugging each other in high glee, they decided on the details of carrying it through.

On the morning of March 6, they took a hansom cab to the home of Bishop W. B. Derrick of the African Methodist Church. The only attendant was the minister's wife. Alice was carrying a small bouquet of pale pink rosebuds, and she looked like one herself in a pale pink dress. Her face was aglow, her bright eyes gleamed with a certain merriment. She was a rosebud and a laughing apple, Paul thought as he took her hand when the bishop nodded to him at the beginning of the service.

At the proper moment he slipped on her finger the gold band she had worn during their engagement. "With this ring I thee wed," he repeated after the bishop.

And so they were married.

Their honeymoon had to be short, but Paul was fairly bursting with happiness on the way back to Washington— Alice was his wife at last! Ma had been in on the secret, yet he wished everyone in the world could know. He had to tell Dr. Tobey at least.

"I am almost afraid to write you," he began the letter, "but out it must come. I am married. I would have consulted you, but the matter was quickly done. People, my wife's parents and others, were doing everything to separate us." He gave the doctor the details of the marriage, and ended, "I hope that you will not think I have been too rash."

Alice could keep the secret no more than Paul. From Brooklyn she wrote to her family, telling them the news. Since she was already married, there was nothing they could do but accept the fact. Free from the biggest obstacle, Paul and Alice didn't want to remain separated any longer. She resigned her teaching post, and started packing for Washington. Paul happily sent a second letter to Dr. Tobey the first week in April:

"I was very glad to get your letter and find that you did not think ill of my step. . . . All has come around all right now and my wife will be with me on the eighteenth. My announcement cards will go out then. Mother is quite enthusiastic, and my mother-in-law has yielded and gracefully accepted the situation.

"Aren't you saying that I had better have got out of debt before taking a wife? Honest, aren't you? Well,

see her and know her and I won't need to make any plea
for myself. Her own personality will do that."

He was sure no man ever had a finer wife nor a better
life than his at the moment. Ma and Alice hit it off right
away. Ma could see from the way Alice looked at Paul
that her new daughter-in-law adored her boy as much as
she, and that was all she asked. And aside from that, she
found Alice a good companion, full of fun; like Paul, she
was always ready to see a joke and laugh at it, a trait Ma
was glad to find. She had secretly been afraid that Alice
might be uppity because of her college education and her
profession, but those fears vanished immediately. "You'd
never know she was a school teacher," Ma remarked ap-
provingly to Paul; and he was so delighted, he bought his
mother a new Easter outfit, "with everything to match,"
as she wrote her sister in Dayton.

He wanted to show Alice off to everybody in Washington. Two days after she arrived, one of his best friends,
Edward Arnold, was married, and suggested that the two
couples have their "turning out" together. "Good!" Paul
agreed. "Next Sunday at St. Luke's." The old custom of
a bride and groom making their first public appearance
would be ideal, he thought.

So the four of them, dressed in their Sunday best, strolled
slowly down the avenue to services the next week. They
saw people nudge each other, and heard the whispers of
"bride-and-groom" from passers-by. Corner cops tipped
their caps, and small shoeshine boys snickered behind their
hands. At the church doors, a bunch of lazy "sinners"
stood around, waiting for a last-minute ogle before the
final bells. As the young couples passed through the doors,
Paul heard one of the idlers call to another, "Hey, there
go the two ugliest grooms and the two prettiest brides I've
ever seen in many a day!"

Paul's friends gave parties for Alice, and of course their next-door neighbors, Judge and Molly Terrell, came over often. Molly had recently been appointed to the Board of Education in Washington, which placed her among the first women, as well as Negroes, to win a post in such an important agency. With the Terrells so close by, Paul and Alice were able to spend many an evening in the kind of talk they both loved—of books, music, art, race problems, world problems. There was trouble in Havana, and rumors of a possible war with Spain ran rife in Washington.

Molly stood in admiration of Paul because he had had financial success with his writing; she had had a few articles published in Negro magazines or political pamphlets on women's rights, but none of them paid.

"The next time you get a check just let me touch it," she said one night when she and the Judge were leaving. So a few days later, when Paul received a check from *Century*, Alice motioned to her from the window, and she came running over. Paul flourished the thin white envelope around his head, opened it and pulled out the check.

"Just let me touch it," Molly repeated, holding out two fingers, and rolling her eyes in comic awe.

They went through the little ceremony, which they never failed to enjoy frequently during the next year or so. For now the flowers of fame began to be heaped upon Paul Dunbar. He was asked to speak before organizations, as well as to give readings. Magazines and newspapers carried articles about him, and by him. The Washington *Post* printed a full column, which called him the "Orpheus of His Race," and included sketches of both Alice and Paul. Magazines asked for short stories and serials, publishing houses for novels. He called these years his "pouring time" because so many opportunities poured in on him from all sides.

Folks from Dixie was published in April, and received very good reviews. The book was dedicated, "To my friend H. A. Tobey, M.D." Paul sent the doctor one of the first copies, enclosing a few lines so like him that his friend had to smile as he read: "I am afraid that the wish to express my gratitude to you and something of the pleasure and pride I take in our friendship have led me to take some liberties with your name. But I can only hope that you will take the dedication in the spirit in which it is offered— that of gratitude, friendship, and respect for the man who has brought light to so many dark hours."

A few days after the book came out, Paul received an invitation to a conference in New York, called by a group of educators for the promotion of college education for Negroes. Paul let his poems speak for him, and they brought him tumultuous applause. One proper Bostonian in the audience, who had come to the conference with every intention of opposing higher education for Negroes, wrote out a check for $1,000 on the spot; if Paul Dunbar was an example of the kind of Negroes colleges could produce, he was happy to make his contribution. Paul nodded graciously and kept a straight face, but he couldn't help wondering what the Bostonian would say if he knew that the closest Paul Dunbar ever came to higher education was the two-man college in the lobby of the Calahan building.

Another man at the conference, who came from Albany, was so taken with Paul's talent, that he lost no time in telling Albany's leading clubwoman that if she wanted to have a successful meeting she should put the young poet on her next program. She sent a wire to Washington at once. Paul was still in New York, consulting Mr. Dodd about a new book of poetry to follow his novel, so Alice opened the telegram while the Western Union boy stood waiting for an answer. "Will come," Alice wrote, accepting the engagement; "fee fifty . . ." She stopped, struck by a sudden impulse: if these people were so anxious to get Paul to come there, they would probably pay more—she crossed out "fifty," and wrote down "one hundred" dollars. The new rate was accepted without question.

By the time Paul came back from Albany, war on Spain had been declared, two months after the battleship *Maine* had been sunk in Havana harbor. Colonel Theodore Roosevelt came to the fore with his regiment of Rough Riders, among them the Negro Tenth Cavalry. When the Ninth Ohio Volunteers was recruited by Major Charles Young, a Dayton classmate of Paul's, two of the first volunteers were Bud Burns and Randy-Tams, who signed up for the medical corps. Paul sent his wishes for a speedy victory and a safe return; he could not enlist because of his health; the cough that had always bothered him had become more insistent since he had started to work in the Library. The war lasted only a few months. Bud and Randy did not see action, but the Negro Tenth was in the thick of the fighting at San Juan Hill, and Theodore Roosevelt praised the gallantry of its troops, which came to the rescue and insured the victory.

Clorindy opened at the Casino Roof Garden in New York early in the summer, bringing additional honors to Paul and Alice, who went up for the opening. The musical was a hit, as Will Cook had predicted. It received rave reviews, and ran until fall, when the company went on tour. Before long, the top tune, "Darktown Is Out To-night" was performed in cafés and nightclubs, hummed and whistled by everybody in town. Paul and Alice, sitting in the author's box on opening night, watched the reaction of the audience: it was "with" the show from the moment the curtain went up—laughing, clapping, keeping time to the syncopated music. And when the chorus came out dancing *and* singing, a positive gasp went up—this was the first time any chorus had ever done both at once! People left the theater smiling, singing snatches of songs, laughing a second time over the funny scenes.

To celebrate their success, Will Cook took Alice and Paul to the Marshall Hotel, where Negro musicians, actors, composers, writers and painters gathered for a good time after the theater, or for dinner on Sunday evening, when an orchestra played. This was Paul's initiation into the night life of New York's Negro society and the group of talented Negroes who were enjoying the spotlight of success. The Marshall was a made-over "brownstone" on West Fifty-third Street. Entertainment was informal on week nights. The piano was never silent for long with musicians around, and sometimes a banjo player joined in, while a ring of revelers formed a circle around them to provide an impromptu chorus.

Sometimes the music was more serious. Harry Burleigh, the composer Paul had met at the Chicago Fair, dropped in one night to try out, in his booming baritone voice, a Negro art song he had just completed. Someone whispered to Paul that as soloist at St. George's Church (a position he would hold for fifty years) he was "packing the pews" every Sunday morning. Later Harry told Paul he had been studying with Anton Dvořák. The maestro had taught him much about composition, and he in turn had shown his teacher the rich, mellow strains in Negro spirituals. Dvorak was so taken with their beauty that he used themes based on their melodies in his *New World Symphony*. Harry wanted to set some of Paul's poems to music—true songs, not minstrel tunes.

Other Broadway celebrities came to the Marshall—Williams and Walker, the vaudeville team, who snapped up the hits from *Clorindy* for their act. Sheet music from the show was published of "Jump Back, Honey," and "Dark-town Is Out Tonight," advertising on the cover, "Origi-nally introduced in the ragtime opera *Clorindy* and now being sung with great success by Williams and Walker." Ford Dabney, who later made a name for himself with his Negro jazz band in Ziegfield shows, stayed at the Marshall when he was in New York; and James Reese Europe, who created dances for Vernon and Irene Castle, stopped in frequently.

Paul enjoyed the stimulating atmosphere of the Marshall, and under the spell of its spotlight glamor, he agreed to write the lyrics for Will Cook's next musical; but back in Washington, he thought better of his promise. He wrote an article on Negro education for the *Independent*, criticiz-ing Tuskegee Institute for its emphasis on industrial train-ing; Paul felt the head was as important as the hand; the Negro's brain as well as his brawn should be recognized. In another piece for the Chicago *Record*, he made an im-passioned plea for the Negro's right to vote. How could he go on grinding out distorted words for minstrel shows? Harry Burleigh had said minstrel tunes were a menace to true Negro music; and Paul felt that these lyrics were a threat to real Negro poetry, even though the ones he had written for *Clorindy* had raised the show above the level of most. (Strictly speaking, *Clorindy* was not a minstrel show, but came closer to musical comedy; it did more than present a series of skits—it told a story, and, long before, paved the way for a folk opera like *Porgy and Bess*.) Will Cook felt much the same as Paul, but he couldn't resist the box-office appeal of shows with a minstrel flavor. Paul could. Alice supported his stand, and after that no amount of persuasion from Will could change his mind.

The Uncalled came out in October, dedicated "To My Wife," and the heroine was named Alice. Paul was deeply

in love, and so was Alice. She was going to have a book
of her own published—a collection of New Orleans legends,
and she could hardly wait till it appeared, for the dedication
read, "To My Husband." She would stand the books side
by side on the mantelpiece.

She was worried about Paul, however. More than once
in the last few months she had awakened in the night to
hear him coughing, a hacking cough that would not cease.
The dust from the musty tomes and medical treatises he
handled in the Library was seeping into his lungs, she was
sure. She convinced him that he could give up the Library,
and earn his living by his writings alone now. *The Uncalled*
had received mixed reviews, but there were enough good
ones, and enough provocative ones to make the book "con-
troversial," so it was selling quite well; *Lyrics of Lowly
Life*, and *Folks from Dixie* were bringing in royalties, and
Paul had nearly completed a second volume of verse for
Dodd, Mead; magazine editors wrote encouraging letters
with requests for stories. Paul's public appearances almost
always brought a good fee since Alice had raised it. "So
I'm sure we can manage," she finished, smiling up at him.
He resigned his post at the Library the first of November.

He settled down to creative work on a full-time basis,
and he had more leisure for entertaining his friends. He
was sought after at parties and professional gatherings; the
Pen and Pencil Club sent him an invitation to join, and he
accepted. Ed Arnold, who belonged to the Bachelor-
Benedict Club, persuaded Paul to joint that club, too. Occasionally he entertained eight or ten of the members at a
buffet supper, after which, if he received the proper in-
ducement, he would stage a wild "war dance" he had once
originated at a party. Ed described the scene in glowing
terms: "He would stand in the center of the floor, his
friends would circle about him, and commence to clap,

pat, shout and chant to the tune of *Georgia Camp Meeting*. Paul would remain motionless for a few seconds, suddenly would leap into the air, and the dance was on. It was a wonderful sight to see him jump up and down with an abandon, a rhythm of movement which showed that his very soul responded to the music of the claps and shouts." He was like a voodoo dancer once he got started, working up to a wild pitch, and ending with a final frenzied leap and a mad shriek, echoed by the others like a war cry until the whole house vibrated with it. Ma and Alice, in an upstairs bedroom, shook their heads, marvelling that the roof didn't cave in.

Paul could give more readings since he was no longer confined to the Library, and he often heard himself introduced as "the poet laureate of the Negro race." He was awarded an honorary degree by Atlanta University, and Tuskegee asked him to compose the verses for its school anthem. During the winter he was called upon for a Lincoln's Day program in New York, given for the benefit of Hampton Institute. Harry Burleigh sang some of his own songs, and the widely known Hampton Quartet gave several numbers. Afterward, Paul decided to drop in on a rehearsal of Will Cook's new show; even though he had refused to finish the lyrics, there were no hard feelings between them, and he was interested in knowing how the production was shaping up. His entrance created quite a stir; James Weldon Johnson, who had taken over the job of writing the lyrics, painted a word-portrait of the poet's arrival: "When he walked into the hall, all those who knew him rushed to welcome him, and among those who did not know him personally there were awed whispers. But it did not appear that celebrity had puffed him up. He met homage with friendly and hearty response. There was no hint of vainglory in his bearing. He sat quiet and unas-

suming while the rehearsal proceeded. He was twenty-
seven, medium height, slim. His black, intelligent face was
grave, almost sad, except when he smiled or laughed. There
was on him the hallmark of distinction. He had an innate
courtliness of manner, his speech was unaffectedly polished
and brilliant, and he carried himself with the dignity of
humility which never fails to produce a sense of the presence of greatness."

From New York, Paul went to Tuskegee, where he had
been invited to a farmers' conference by President Booker
Washington; he was also covering the conference for the
Philadelphia *Press*. One of the faculty conducting the
meeting was Professor George Washington Carver, who
had become a "name" in science in the six years since the
World's Fair, and would go on to much greater fame before his career was over. On the way back north, Paul had
several engagements—at Knoxville College, Spelman, and
Hampton Institute, and everywhere he was welcomed as
a "figure," a famous personality. "But I don't *feel* famous,"
he said afterward to Alice.

He met her in Boston, where she had gone to visit her
family while Paul was in the South. Although it was mean
March weather, the Moores had taken a cottage on the
Mystic River outside of Boston for a week's fishing. Paul
didn't catch any fish; in the raw, blustery wind, unfortunately, all he caught was a cold; he gave up in disgust.
The wind shoved him indoors, shivering; he spent the rest
of the day romping with little Leila, Alice's niece. In the
evening, the howls of the gale grew stronger, making a
weird sound like a ghost outside.

"There's the Boogah Man, Uncle Paul—the Boogah
Man!" Leila ran to him, frightened, as a sudden gust swept
around the corner of the house.

"Shucks, the Boogah Man won't hurt good little girls

like you." He hugged her tight and laughed, remembering
how he had tried to frighten his brothers when he was
about Leila's age.

"Tell me 'bout the Boogah Man, Uncle Paul," she said,
now that she was safely snuggled in his arms. So he began
to make up a poem, his eyes half-closed, thinking it out;
his voice was low and mysterious:

> W'en de evening shadders
> Come a-glidin' down,
> Fallin' black an' heavy
> Over hill an' town. . . .
>
> Den you'll hyeah a funny
> Soun' ercross de lan';
> Lay low; dat's de callin'
> Of de Boogah Man!
>
> Woo-oo, woo-oo!

A high-pitched giggle of shivery delight came from Leila,
and she snuggled down farther.

> Hide yo' little peepers 'hind yo' han';
> Woo-oo, woo-oo!
> Callin' of de Boogah Man.

For a "good little girl" like Leila, he ended comfortingly:

> But you needn' bothah
> 'Bout de Boogah Man!

Paul's cold was heavy on his chest the next morning, but
he had engagements in Rochester, Newton, and Philadelphia, so he pushed on. Alice, who went back to Washington by herself, found *Lyrics of the Hearthside* waiting, and
saw with some amazement that it was dedicated, "To
Alice." Paul hadn't told her he was going to dedicate a
second book to her.

He was tickled at having sprung a surprise on her, and pleased with the book when he saw it. He received letters of congratulations and praise from all sides. Some of his best poems were here: "Lullaby," "Little Brown Baby," which was set to music, "Angelina," "At Candle Lightin' Time," "Whistlin' Sam," with the notes of a melody right in it.

The spring was chilly, and Paul's cold persisted, but he kept on with his work—writing, speaking before various groups, giving recitals. On April 21, Walter Damrosch, the noted conductor-composer, who had set Paul's "The Deserted Plantation" to music, was going to put the piece on a program at the Waldorf-Astoria; and a week later Paul was to go to Albany again for a reading, where he was to be presented by Governor Theodore Roosevelt. Some people made fun of "Teddy" Roosevelt and his reforms, but Paul admired him very much. He was looking forward to both events when he left on a tour of engagements in the mid-West beforehand. Alice was worried about his traveling with such a stubborn cold, but he promised to take care of himself.

The day he reached New York, however, he was feeling so wretched and feverish he couldn't even attend the concert, let alone consider going on to Albany. He went directly to Mrs. Matthews, the kind friend who had conspired with him to get Alice to the bon voyage party; after one look at his gaunt face, she put him to bed, called a doctor, and sent a telegram to Alice: "Come at once."

Paul had pneumonia. For days he hovered between life and death; the papers reported his condition as "crucial"; he might go at any moment. As soon as the news was out, notes, messages, calls, flowers came flooding in from everywhere. William Dean Howells came to see if he could do anything to help. Dr. Tobey, Bud and Rob all sent letters full of concern; Bud was practicing medicine now and offered what advice he could at such a distance. Ma, back in Washington, was nearly crazy with worry, and couldn't see why she shouldn't be with her son at such a time. But Alice was giving him every care, and there wasn't room at Mrs. Matthews for another person; Paul should have been in a hospital, but the doctors said it would be dangerous to move him.

He was seriously ill for over a month, and Alice tended him all during the long days and nights until the doctors insisted that a nurse come in to help. When Paul finally began to recover, the doctor's verdict was still grave: his lungs were affected, and he needed at least six months' rest, preferably in the mountains. Bud seconded this advice, and warned Paul against accepting Rob's invitation to come to Chicago to recuperate—the climate there was too humid. Alice had a difficult time locating a place that would fit their pocketbook, but she finally found one in the Catskills, and Bud came from Ohio to join them. He was there as both friend and doctor, and kept an eye on Paul's progress in the next few weeks while the three went fishing, boating, and picnicking. Paul's spirits began to improve the first day, when he caught five fish. His appetite was better, too, and his weight went back up to one hundred and twenty-five pounds.

As soon as he was stronger, the "itch to write" came back. He was able to send *Harper's Weekly* a 3,000-word article on Negro life in Washington, which he had promised the magazine before his illness; he also finished two stories he had started, and composed two or three poems.

In the fall, Paul was ready to return to Washington, but the doctor told him after a check-up that he must go to Colorado for the winter; he needed at least six months' more rest in a high, dry climate. He and Alice made plans for the trip; they would rent the house in Washington, and this time Ma would go with them. Paul lined up writing assignments for the long stay. George Horace Lorimer, editor of the *Saturday Evening Post*, suggested that Paul write a series of stories around one or two of his well-known characters like Aunt Tempe, Aunt Doshy and Uncle Ike. *Lippincott's* wanted a light novel, to be published serially; and the Denver *Post* sent a telegram proposing a tour of Colorado at their expense; Paul could be a kind of roving reporter for the paper while he was in the state. This Paul felt would be too strenuous for someone trying to get over a serious bout with tuberculosis, but when the editor made a more liberal proposition, offering to pay Alice's expenses as well as his, saying that he need write only the articles he felt like doing, he accepted.

They found a sunny little house in Harmon, just outside of Denver, and settled down to spend the winter. The doctor had warned Paul against much exercise—he could do very little walking, and certainly no bicycling; a small amount of riding wouldn't hurt him. So Paul went to the livery stable to look for a horse and buggy.

"No high-stepping thoroughbred for me," he told the man. "I need one more on the order of 'the old gray mare.'" He grinned.

Luckily, the liveryman had just that—an old mare who had been around so long she knew every road in the neighborhood.

One look at old "Sukey" told Paul she was for him, and he bought an ancient buggy to match his bony, sway-back mare. Sometimes he took Ma and Alice riding, but Sukey was too pokey for them, so he got himself a saddle, bit and bridle, and let old Sukey go sashaying around the countryside with him—she knew all the roads, and she always brought him home eventually. She was put into one of his most successful poems before long, "Dat Ol' Mare O' Mine," which brought Paul half of what he paid for her from *Century*.

He began to write a Western novel, *The Love of Landry*, a romance about a young girl who comes to Colorado for her health, gets mixed up with a cowboy and a cattle stampede before she is cured, and of course, finds happiness as well as health. It was light reading, designed for a magazine, just the sort of work Paul needed while he was regaining his own health. To describe the cattle stampede, he went to Major William Cooke Daniels, a friend of Dr. Tobey who became Paul's friend as well. He offered Paul the use of his library, and the two spent many hours together in good talk, smoking the Major's fine cigars. He knew his native state well, and was able to fill in details for Paul about the actions of both the frightened, angry herd and the riders in the stampede scene. When the novel came out in book form, Paul dedicated it "To my friend Major William Cooke Daniels in memory of some pleasant days spent over this little story."

He was feeling better but he still spent many sleepless nights when the cough would not let him rest. Yet even in those long hours, his mind was at work, thinking, bringing to life rich scenes in poetry and prose. One night, lying there in the darkness, he heard the dull thudding of a thousand hoofbeats across the plains; several hundred "head of cattle" were being driven to market by watchful riders. Paul couldn't see them, he could only hear the plodding sound of their slow passage and, in his mind, a picture formed—he saw a pageant of people—his own—struggling with slow footsteps to reach the light from the dark depths of slavery, inequality, prejudice. In case the thought should slip his mind if he fell asleep, he got out of bed and lit the small lamp above his night table.

> Slow moves the pageant of a climbing race,
>> [he wrote]
> Their footsteps drag far, far below the height . . .

Before dawn he had completed a poem, which ended with
a spur:

> Heed not the darkness round you, dull and deep;
> The clouds grow thickest when the summit's nigh.

Except for a quick trip East, to take Ma to Chicago, and
to go to New York on business, Paul and Alice were in
Colorado until spring. He started a new novel, *The Fanatics*, wrote several articles for the Denver *Post*, and one or
two stories; and in between, the wellsprings of poetry were
always bubbling. There seemed to be no end for his capac-
ity to write, although his energy at times ebbed low, and
Alice would urge him to rest more. But how could he rest,
with so much to say still inside him?

In May, when the weather was pleasantest in Chicago
and the East, Paul decided it was a good time to visit his
family and take care of his affairs, although the doctor ad-
vised him not to stay in the city for long; when the weather
became humid, he must go to the Catskills again. Alice
saw to it that "doctor's orders" were carried out. They
stopped to see Ma, and Rob's new baby, named Paul, after
his famous uncle, went on to Toledo for a visit with the
Tobeys, and to Washington, to look after the house before
taking off for the mountains. Paul felt fine—he was up to
a hundred and forty-five, the most he had ever weighed in
his twenty-eight years.

The mountains were fresh and cool after the steaminess
of Washington. Paul could do much more than the first
time they had come to the Catskills, so besides the fishing,
which was always good, he and Alice enjoyed the hiking

through wooded hills. Paul found himself a crooked branch
to lean on—"my alpenstock," he told Alice grandly.

Paul's June statement from Dodd, Mead brought good
news: *Lyrics of Lowly Life* had sold nearly twelve thousand copies; *Cabin and Field* close to five thousand—more
than any poet, except perhaps James Whitcomb Riley
or Eugene Field. The June issue of *Current Literature* magazine carried Paul's picture on the cover; inside
he was featured as their monthly "American Poet of Today." Other honors kept coming. He was elected to the
American Social Science Association for distinction in literature. E. C. Stedman asked Paul's permission to include
several of the poems in his anthology of American literature. *Century* accepted half a dozen poems at once, and
Mr. Johnson wanted Paul's opinion as to whether the magazine overdid the Negro as a comedian. Paul thought not.
"There is a large humorous quality in his character just
as there is in that of the Irishman," he explained in his
answer, "and I cannot see that a laugh, when one laughs
with them, hurts either one or the other."

By fall Alice and Paul were back in Washington, where
Ma joined them. Paul didn't want to go to Colorado again
if he could avoid it, but he had to be extremely careful;
he gave up the recital tours for the most part, and concen-
trated on writing. (Others were giving the readings for
him: he heard that in the South, Negro students working
their way through college earned their expenses by presenting programs of his poems at hotels and clubs. He was
glad to know that his work was helping to give young
scholars the college education he had missed.)

He finished his novel, *The Fanatics*, a story of southern
sympathizers before the Civil War, by Christmas time; and
early in the new year—1901, the first of a new century—

Lippincott's magazine asked him for a full-length novel to be published in their May issue. He already had one planned—*Sport of the Gods* he was going to call it—a realistic picture of a young southern Negro who comes to New York, and gets caught in the whirlpool of New York life. He wrote furiously, and inside of a month had set down fifty thousand words, nearly a full-length novel. The story seemed to rush out of him, like his poetry. The characters "moved by themselves," and he had to work fast to keep up with them.

One evening after dinner, he was in the study putting the final touches on the book, when he heard the doorbell ring. Alice was speaking to a man; Paul cocked one ear to listen, but the voice wasn't familiar. He caught a word or two "... President McKinley ... Inaugural Day ..." And then Alice was ushering in a White House dignitary, who carried in his chamois-gloved hand a scroll-like document—an official communication from the President to Paul Dunbar, inviting the poet to take part in the Inaugural Day parade, with the honorary rank of Colonel!

There was only one question, the messenger went on: Could Mr. Dunbar furnish his own horse for the parade? Paul smiled as a picture of old Sukey, meandering down Massachusetts Avenue while the procession swept past her, rose in his mind. But Sukey had been sold when they left Colorado; and the thought of riding some strange horse, who might possibly shy when the band started up sent Paul into a panic. He was sorry, he told the messenger. He was honored, but he would not be able to make it. Regretfully but firmly, he showed the man out.

The door was hardly shut when Ma and Alice popped out from behind the parlor drapes; they had heard every word, and before he could scold them for listening, they pounced on him.

"You out'n your mind, boy?" Ma said.

"You must go!" Alice commanded.

He couldn't get a word in edgewise to explain.

"Tell him you changed your mind."

"Send a note to the White House."

"Call him up."

"Go after him." This last was from Alice, and with the thought, she ran to the window. The messenger was still on the doorstep, carefully rerolling the document into a long cylinder.

"Quick! You can still catch him!" She gave Paul a push. Helpless, he let himself be shoved outside in his smoking-jacket and slippers, and apologetically told the messenger he would be able to accept the invitation after all. The man didn't seem in the least surprised.

"He must be married," Paul said slyly to Alice when he came indoors.

But he really didn't mind the way she had bossed him into going. Inauguration Day dawned clear and bright, and he found the livery-stable horse steady, easy to manage. As the parade marched along Massachusetts Avenue, Paul was very glad Alice had insisted that he take part in it. The sun was shining, the bands were playing, the flags were flying high. Along the street white and colored citizens alike stood watching the Inaugural Day parade. When it passed a certain corner, he knew Alice and Ma would be there in the crowd, waving—he could even see the top of Alice's blue hat. He kept his face to the front, his back straight; but he raised his riding crop in a gesture that said plainly to her: "Howdy, honey, howdy!"

In a few short years, Paul would lose the private battle he was fighting with those "little, red, hair-like devils," as Robert Louis Stevenson had called them, which were hacking away at his lungs. He would give up the long struggle finally, on February 9, 1906.

Today, however, he was feeling quite well, almost strong again, perhaps from the very fact that he was an honorary colonel in the Presidential procession. He remembered suddenly the first time he had heard the story of the knight and the Holy Grail from Ma, and how he used to imagine himself setting out on a white horse, riding, riding, riding . . .

Well, he wasn't astride a fine white steed—just an old brown mare from the livery stable—but his quest was as sacred as the search for the Holy Grail. He was seeking the cup of true freedom for his people. The obstacles he had to battle were still great, but he would help to conquer them—not with a sword, but a song!

Jean Gould was born in Darke County, Ohio, only about forty miles from Dayton, the birthplace of Paul Laurence Dunbar, so it was not surprising that she came to know his poetry at an early age. She remembers her grade school teachers reading "Little Brown Baby" and "The Boogah Man" and being captivated by their combination of the comfortable with the mysterious—an association that all children love.

After her college years at the University of Michigan and Toledo University, Miss Gould turned to writing and eventually to juvenile books, her most recent being *Young Mariner Melville*, a biography of the author of *Moby Dick*. Like Dunbar, she left her native state to come to New York, but, unlike him, she settled down in one place, in Greenwich Village, and she has been writing in the same spot ever since.

In her free time, Miss Gould likes to garden and to paint watercolors but claims to have more love than talent for either one. She also enjoys cooking, at which she says she is much more successful.

She decided to write about Paul Dunbar because he had a singularly happy school career, and she thought that this would be a good time to retell his story, "which might set an example for school children everywhere."